In Memory of
Bill Spagnola

Bill was a friend from childhood. We worked, fished and spent endless hours discussing human behavior with an open dialog about life and its rewards and pitfalls. Bill was perhaps the most versatile and creative friend I was privileged to know. Sadly, he passed never really being recognized for his creative thinking that manifested in the world of photography, woodworking and all outdoor activities.

Enjoy your trip down
"The Dusty Trail"

Ray Hazel

Dedication to
Lighthouse of Manasota, Florida

This book was made possible through the efforts and services which are offered free of charge by the Lighthouse of Manasota. This agency and staff are dedicated to working with low vision and blind individuals.

Their staff designed a process which allowed me the luxury of accomplishing my sincere desire to write, despite my low vision, and I regained the confidence and ability to persevere. Their services, coupled with a staff of certified teachers dedicated to helping people with vision issues, allowed me to continue being a positive contributor to society. Anyone suffering from these issues should take advantage of this tremendous organization.

Special Acknowledgments

Jane Tirrell

During this process, my companion, Jane, displayed patience and tolerated endless hours of my compulsion to write this book whenever I was motivated. Her ability to encourage this effort allowed me to stay focused. Jane's literary background was most beneficial during moments when writer's cramp surfaced. The objective and Jane's honest constructive suggestions were welcomed and non-threatening. Without her understanding and sacrifice, this effort perhaps would have died a slow death in my brain and on my computer. Words cannot express my gratitude.

Joyce Horecki

This effort would never have evolved without my friend and neighbor, Joyce Horecki. Her expert editing, coupled with positive reinforcement, inspired me to continue when motivation was lacking. She realized that my acute low vision occasionally became an issue that required patience and tolerance. Her honest, sincere empathy regarding vision issues always helped me to embrace this effort with renewed optimism and motivation. The process required long hours and hard work. Joyce always looked at this manuscript realizing the primary objective. It's rare to find a friend who stays the course during difficult trying times. Thank you Joyce for staying the course.

Judy Boylan

Judy was my computer teacher who works for The Lighthouse of Manasota. Without her persistence and dedication, this novel would have remained just a dream.

Bob Goebel

Bob is a friend and neighbor who helped me with problems associated with computer technology and printers. Special thanks.

Cynthia Puente

Cindy, my sister, always helped keep this effort in perspective. Her grasp of purpose was always refreshing.

Mike Hazel

My son inspired this book. His ability to understand and discuss the primary purpose always came from a positive perspective.

Rich Horecki

His analytical approach to life always brought an honest, sincere approach to the logistics of this book.

Sally Myers

Sally was a resource in helping me deal with vision issues. I knew she supported this effort honestly. There's security and comfort in her dedication to helping me deal with low vision.

Deni Abbott

This friend always made my life easier and less complicated when I needed information or help adjusting to life in Florida. Thanks.

Winnie

My modern literature teacher wasn't capable of placing principles before personalities. From that experience, I learned the difference between grammar and creativity.

Table of Contents

CHAPTER 1

My Uncle Lee

At the ripe old age of eleven going on twelve, I started to show signs of a serious addiction for the love of nature and wildlife. In reality, I was cursed at a very early age with the self-inflicted addiction that Jack London so appropriately named in his title, "Call of the Wild." This addiction was a curse that went back at least five generations. It all started when I was least expecting the introduction to a lifestyle that has followed me throughout my seventy years. At the time the addiction started creeping into my existence, my family lived next door to my Great-Uncle Leon, who served as my dad's father and my grandfather. Behind a very modest house was a two-car garage, with half of it serving as a firewood shed and the other half also divided, leaving room for a small car. The remainder served as what would be considered in today's terms as my uncle's man cave. That man cave was off-limits to me, and I knew if I ever entered that territory the consequences would be grave. With all the activity that took place in that cave, you can only imagine the urge and compulsion that was building in the mind of an eleven-year-old.

One September morning I was playing outside between my great-uncle's garage and my dad's carport. I could see smoke coming out of the chimney located above the man cave. An odor that I was not familiar with hung in the warm, humid fall air. I could hear pounding and chains rattling, which piqued my curiosity, but I knew any attempt to wander over toward that forbidden territory would bring down the wrath of God. In the mind of an eleven-year-old, I can remember trying to conjure up a plan that could help me gain access; however, fear and common sense prevailed! As I wandered toward the two foxhounds that served as my family pets, they started barking with excitement, and that's when my uncle appeared from out of nowhere and told me the dogs need water and some dog food. With reverence, I stated that I had already fed them and they had tipped over their water dishes. My uncle uttered, "If the bowls tipped over, then they were empty." He had a way of getting to the point without inflicting serious humiliation. My uncle walked back toward his cave, but to my surprise, he got into his 1946 green Nash and headed down the gravel street. I thought at the time he had left for the business that he owned-his liquor store. While I carried water for the dogs, I couldn't help but notice that the sliding doors to the garage were left open and the door to the cave was ajar. My chance had arrived, and after watering the dogs, I slowly worked my way along the side of the forbidden territory. With every step I was filled with emotions ranging from fear to unrelenting curiosity. Slipping into the garage, the smell of the cave was just a few yards away. I can still feel the fear that if I got caught my life wouldn't be worth a plug nickel. With reckless abandon and to my own surprise, I walked slowly and confidently into a world that was about to change my life forever.

That morning I was wearing a grey flannel shirt tucked into my Levi jeans that were patched on both knees. I was average height for my age, but very thin. I appeared to be all gristle and muscle from constantly moving and playing with my hounds. My hair was dark brown with a double cowlick, making it stand up in the back regardless of attempts by my mom to eliminate the problem. It didn't bother me, and I couldn't understand why it bothered females so much. My face was covered with freckles and I had perfect teeth that accentuated my permanent grin. My smile was an asset which I had learned at a very early age could get attention, as well as help get me out of trouble on occasion! I always wore black, high-top Converse sneakers that were usually at least one size too big. Energy was my strong suit, which caused me difficulty since I was curious and very observant.

Slowly opening the door wider, I stepped inside and was confronted with an unexpected spectacle of a multitude of tools and an assortment of metal objects that were partly rusty. I observed several wooden boards that were shaped strangely at one end. These boards were stained, as if coffee had been poured on them. These boards were different lengths, thicknesses and widths. Walking toward the workbench, I noticed a strange metal object was fastened in a vice and the chain hung with a circle ring on the end. There were several of these objects on the bench and they varied in sizes. The potbelly stove had a small barrel sitting on top, and it was steaming with the odor that I smelled outside, but much more pungent. The liquid was as black as a new stovepipe, and in my confusion I suddenly felt that I wasn't alone. I turned around slowly and there he was. The vision of my uncle was burned into my soul, and after 64 years I remember how he looked at that moment. He was wearing a red flannel shirt and green dickey pants that were two sizes too big, and they were held up with heavy green suspenders. He had old rubber green packs on his feet that had been cut off just above the ankles. He wore a red hunting cap cocked on the side of his head and he sported a five-day growth that was salt and pepper colored like his thinning hair. Standing there caught red-handed, I had the sudden urge to pee! Uncle Lee reached into his back pocket, took out his red patterned handkerchief and wiped the side of his mouth where the plug of Yankee Girl chew had run down his chin, and he softly asked if I had watered the dogs. I said, "Yes sir."

With a grin on his face, he walked slowly toward me and reached out and affectionately patted my head. He said, "Go tell your mother where you're going to be and put on an old shirt and jeans. I wondered how long it would take you to work your way into my trapper's shed."

After doing what I was told, I ran back to the shed to wallow in the comfort of my great-uncle. When I arrived, he handed me a cold root beer and said, "Now that you're here, you might as well give me a hand."

Taking a drink, I uttered with excitement, "What would you like me to do?"

He slowly removed the rusty strangely shaped metal object and he handed it to me. Reaching out and wrapping my small hand around the chain, he softly stated, "This is a number one jump trap for muskrats." I had no idea what a muskrat was, but I knew now what a number one jump trap looked like. He handed me a small wire brush and asked me to brush the heavy rust off the trap. Pulling up a stool, he gently lifted me up so I could work at his bench. I worked diligently at my assignment, but it was difficult, as I continued to pick myself with the wire brush. My uncle noticed and asked if I was bleeding.

He then added, "Your mom will kill me if you get hurt in here." Out of fear of having to answer to my mom, he suggested that I simply observe. He manipulated several traps in the calm, gentle manner that I loved about this rustic old man.

After performing his task, he quietly told me to sit in the old tan recliner and said he would be right back. He didn't have to remind me not to touch anything, as that was a forgone conclusion. A short time later, my uncle walked back into the shed carrying a large bag and box. Putting the bag and box on the floor, he asked me if I felt it was time to go on a fox hunt, and I was extremely excited. I was so surprised at the question all I could do was nod yes. Reaching into the bag, he pulled out a pair of red Ballard hunting pants and told me to pull them on over my old jeans. Due to my excitement, I was having some difficulty. He kept watching me wrestle with the pants and finally, softly said, "Your pants might go on easier if you removed your sneakers," which I did. With my new hunting pants on, he handed me a matching jacket and hat. With a smile on his face, he also handed me a pair of green rubber packs that were just like his, and he calmly suggested that I try them on and they fit. With a sense of satisfaction evident on his weather beaten face, he asked what dog I would like to run in the morning and I chose my family pet, Freckles. Uncle Lee responded that I had made a good choice. "He's as good a foxhound as any to be found anywhere in the whole state."

Taking my hand, we walked out into the sunlight. Uncle Lee asked what seemed to be a strange question. "Ray, would you like to go pick some late blackberries?"

I asked, "Where are they?"

He responded, "If you can get permission from your mom and promise not to tell anyone where these berries are, we will go." It was at that moment that I realized my relationship with my uncle had suddenly evolved into a dimension of life where he trusted me with information and wanted to share his secret fall berry patch with me and me alone. That is when my love and respect for my uncle was returned, coupled with honesty and integrity being a primary premise that would always remain engrained in our love for each other. That is probably when it all started.

After gaining permission and grabbing a long-sleeve shirt-a necessity for blackberry picking-I ran toward the green Nash. The inside of this old car consisted of some Yankee Girl chew and a Folgers coffee can lined with cheesecloth used as a spittoon sitting on the passenger's side floorboard. Sitting on the edge of the seat so I could see out the windows, I remember feeling loved and happy. Uncle Lee told me to get my berry pail from the floor of the back seat and after some difficulty, I found an old metal pail that had a wire handle attached, and inside the pail I found a pair of small leather gloves with the tips of each finger and thumbs cut off at the first knuckle. When I asked why these gloves were cut he laughed and said, "The last time we went picking you spent more time picking barbs out of your fingers than you did picking berries!" The other thing that he stated was that he required four quarts for my mother to make a berry pie. Then he insulted me by inferring that I wasn't allowed to eat more berries than I picked. He reached over and patted my knee as if to apologize.

As we headed to the berry patch, our conversation subsided as he kept looking diligently for a turnoff that wasn't more than a hundred yards down the street. Pulling into an old deserted farm driveway, he slowly drove behind the vacant old chicken coop. It was then that he said, "This will hide the car." I learned something about my uncle at that moment.

As we got out of the vehicle with our buckets, I said, "This is the start of the Dusty Trail," and he asked me how this trail got named. I replied that I often played down here with Freckles and I named it. He laughed out loud and explained that when he was my age, he had played in the same area and he had called it the Orchard Path.

I told my uncle I liked the name Dusty Trail better and he said, "Dusty Trail it is." As we walked slowly toward the berry patch, it was evident that our mission was not in vain, since I could see berries hanging on the bushes. Uncle Lee said, "You know, Ray, most people are in such a hurry to get somewhere they never see or appreciate where they are or where they've been."

I was confused and asked, "What do you mean?"

Putting on his leather gloves, he asked me if I noticed anything around the old chicken coop, and I replied the only thing I noticed were some raspberry bushes and he responded, "You're absolutely right, and that's what I meant. You're very aware of your surroundings and that will help you later in life."

As we started picking, he reminded me that I should pick off one bush at a time and then move on. He had pointed that out on a previous picking trip and I realized that he always knew that my quest to please often caused me to hurry, which had gotten me in trouble on several occasions.

After we finished filling our buckets and our bellies with berries, he hitched up his green dickeys, which never seemed to help, since his suspenders drew them back to the same location. Walking back side-by-side with two pails of blackberries, my uncle referred to the fox hunt planned for the morning and my excitement was evident, because he softly told me that no guns were going to be used, and my heart sunk. "Let me explain why we won't use guns. Freckles needs training, and your mom wouldn't allow you to go otherwise." I wasn't fond of my mom at that moment and my uncle realized my disappointment and lifted my spirits by explaining what I already knew; that mothers were very protective for obvious reasons.

Driving back to our homes with relaxed satisfaction, Uncle Lee gave me instructions for preparing Freckles for his morning training run. I was to feed him around suppertime, along with plenty of water. Uncle Lee reached into his pocket and handed me a small bag. He told me to give the contents to my pet after he drank. I looked into my uncles eyes and for the first time, I realized that his eyes were the same color as mine. The contents of the bag were some sort of high-protein dog food that Freckles would need for the next three weeks because Uncle Lee had entered my pet in the State Foxhound Championships, which was news to me. At the time, I didn't get the significance of what had just transpired, but I would find out in a few weeks.

CHAPTER 2

My Family

Back at home during supper that evening, my dad and I discussed the day's events, and there was an awkward moment when I thought I saw a tear in his eye that he tried to hide. I was suddenly fearful. My dad had never shown that type of emotion in my presence in my short memory. My mom quickly changed the subject to blackberry pies, giving my dad time to recover his composure. My five-year-old sister, Cindy, shifted nervously and awkwardly turned in her chair. She loved Freckles and sensed that this was an important conversation.

Speaking of Mom, she was a very pretty lady with very fine features. She was very well coordinated and enjoyed all outdoor activities. Discipline and hard work were prevalent in her personality, and her hair was prematurely grey and wavy. Everyone joked that her hair started turning grey after I was born, and there was probably more truth than fiction regarding this comment. My mother was just over five-foot, but appeared taller due to her hairstyle and trim frame. Her eyes were grey, which always gave her mood and disposition away. She was brutally honest and expected respect in return. I always knew right where she stood on all fronts, and for that matter every family member treated her with kid gloves. My parents seemed to be compatible, making life expectations consistent. You didn't have to guess about Mom's opinions on most subjects.

My sister Cindy always seemed in control of her feelings and was capable of dealing with life on life's terms. She was thin like me, with freckles, but her hair was thick, making it difficult for mom to braid. There was always a battle over that process. My sister was stubborn to a fault, which oftentimes got her into trouble with Mom, but never Dad. I knew that my sister manipulated Dad, making life so interesting. My sis was more tomboy than she admitted, but it made our relationship easy and usually enjoyable. I need to accent the word *usually*.

One characteristic I understood was her honesty and ability to keep secrets from Mom, but never Dad. We really enjoyed messing with our parents and often collaborated for the sheer fun of it.

After supper, I went out to feed the hounds and Dad accompanied me, which didn't happen that often, so it was pleasant. My dad was medium height, and he usually wore jean shirts with matching Levi jeans. His hair was jet black and naturally wavy, which he combed back without a part. He was thin, but rugged-looking, and he always carried himself with confidence and ease, which was often mistaken for arrogance. My father also had a smile that was infectious. One thing that I was grateful for was that he hated suspenders like I did. He usually wore brown work boots that were always well worn. His hands were strong, and he always had his right hand in his jean pocket while he constantly rattled his chain and keys, which irritated my mom. That habit was usually an indication that he was deep in thought. His deep hazel eyes accented his good looks and made him appear warmly handsome and kind.

After Freckles drank, I gave him the two biscuits as instructed. Taking my hand and looking at me with love and respect, my father informed me that he decided not to join us in the morning training run. I was surprised and perplexed. With some difficulty, I asked why; I assumed he had to work, but that wasn't the answer I got.

With emotion surfacing in my father's demeanor, he struggled with an answer that satisfied me and eased my confusion. He said, "You know Ray, that Uncle Lee never married and never had a son. He helped raise ten of your aunts and uncles after my father died." I knew about that; however; at the age of eleven it had never seemed significant until now. My father continued, "You and your Uncle Lee have a very understanding friendship and you both will enjoy your new hunting outfit. You're about to experience something with your uncle that he deserves to share with you. This is something he has wanted to experience his entire life. You may be too young to understand and appreciate the entire process; but the two of you will work together to prepare Freckles for the competition." At that time I asked my dad why Uncle Lee wanted to enter my pet. Dad responded, "Uncle Lee has a desire to prove that Freckles is a special foxhound."

I replied with, "Freckles is blind in one eye and doesn't look like the other hounds I've seen."

Dad responded, "That's the point, and while you work with your uncle and Freckles, you're going to better understand this obsession which your uncle is so fixated on. I want you to simply do as he asks. Uncle Lee is getting older, and you're very special in his eyes. Someday when you're older, you'll be grateful for his attention."

That evening as I washed up for bed, my anticipation for the morning was similar to the excitement I experienced on Christmas Eve. Sleep wasn't going to come easy. With my parents tucking my sister and me into bed after prayers, my mom informed me that the plans were for my uncle and me to leave around nine o'clock. She said that breakfast would be around eight and then she reminded me that she had packed a lunch for the two of us. After thanking her, I blurted out something that surprised me as much as it shocked her. "I don't understand why everyone is acting so differently."

Sitting on the end of my bed and wringing her hands, she reached out and patted my feet and replied, "Try to understand that your Uncle Lee and your dad need this experience for reasons too complicated to understand, but your future development and happiness will be served." She was correct; I sure as hell didn't understand what she meant.

CHAPTER 3

The Training Run

The morning came quickly and excitement was evident but noticeably subdued. After eating breakfast, my dad told me that it was going to be too warm for my new hunting pants, but I was to wear the jacket and hat. He left the decision about the boots up to me. I walked onto the porch with our lunches and looked for my uncle. I heard the car door slam and car start.

Walking toward my pet, Freckles started to bark and Uncle Lee hollered over that he had a chain for Freckles and I responded that he didn't need any chain. Unlocking the snap to my dog's collar, Freckles walked diligently at my side, and when the door was opened he hopped in as if he knew what was happening, and I believe he did. Uncle Lee told me to get in the back seat with the dog and when I sat down, Freckles put his head on my lap and looked up at me with the one eye.

I patted my pet and asked my uncle where we were going. He answered, "The meadow down by the Pontoon Bridge."

I asked, "Why there?"

The answer was, "There's a den of foxes on the back side of the meadow near the end of the rock fence." He asked if I remembered running his rabbit hound in the area, and the answer was yes.

We were suddenly pulling into a meadow, and after he shut off the Nash, he slowly turned his head and replied, "There

13

are five foxes in this area, because the young ones haven't been thrown out of the den yet. Freckles shouldn't have any problems starting a fox." Freckles was sound asleep on my lap and Uncle Lee laughed and said, "You might want to wake him unless you're planning on chasing the fox yourself!" We both laughed and Freckles came alive.

Getting out of the car, it was warm outside, just as my dad predicted. Freckles and I met Uncle Lee in front of the Nash. Freckles walked beside me, and that's when my uncle asked how we were going to get Freckles interested in foxes and not me. I responded that he knows why he's here, and I'm just going to tell him it's okay to chase some foxes. My uncle said to give it a try. Looking at Freckles, I pointed toward the meadow and said, "Go get them."

He immediately started trotting with his head down, working the meadow that was full of goldenrod and I heard my uncle say, "Well, I'll be damned." Uncle Lee said that if he hadn't seen that with his own eyes he wouldn't have believed it.

Grabbing our lunches, we headed for the end of the meadow, which was covered with goldenrod and dead flowers, and my eyes started to run. There was no sign of Freckles, but I knew if my uncle was correct about his observation it wasn't going to take long for him to hit a fresh track. After reaching a spot that had been previously determined by my uncle, we sat down with our backs braced against the stone wall. It was the first time I noticed that my uncle wasn't so agile, and my dad's reference to his age became apparent. Poking me and pointing toward the other side of the meadow, he asked if I could see a broken gate between the rail fence, and I could. He said that when Freckles gets on a fox he should bring him from that direction, because this area is surrounded by water and it's only four miles around. These foxes usually run in a wide circle due to the fact that they live and survive with little interference.

Reaching for my lunch, my attention was diverted by the bark of Freckles, which was music to my uncle's ears and brought a unique smile to his face as his entire body came alive with excitement. He reached for my hand and squeezed it firmly. Talking low, he said, "This will be your first experience with your friend that will change your feelings and respect for Freckles forever." The barking continued, and every once in a while there was a very noticeable difference in his bark. My uncle told me that was because Freckles was getting closer to the fox. My heart was beating and I kept looking toward the bark. My uncle had told me to watch ahead of the bark by the length of a football field because the fox is out front and trying to shake him. This went on for what seemed like hours and there was no sight of a fox or Freckles. Needless to say, I was worried, and it obviously showed.

That's when Uncle Lee explained that Freckles was running the old dog fox. With a troubled look on my uncle's face, the problem suddenly seemed magnified, yet he wasn't disturbed. I reluctantly asked what difference it made if Freckles was chasing an old dog fox or any other fox. He smiled and graciously said, "That old fox has been hunted with dogs before, and he's going to give Freckles a problem." Stepping out into the meadow, Uncle Lee looked around and told me to follow him, and we slowly started in the direction of the broken gate that he had pointed out earlier. The barking had stopped and that was not a good sign, meaning one of two things could have happened. The fox either holed up or Freckles lost him. All of a sudden, a bellow echoed and that little S.O.B. had the fox cornered. I knew instantly that what was transpiring hadn't been expected. Freckles wouldn't give up on the fox until he couldn't go any more. That dog had more heart than any hound I had ever seen.

Suddenly, out of the corner of my eye, a flash grabbed my attention and I yelled to my uncle that I could see the fox running on top of the stone fence, and when Uncle Lee turned quickly, he yelled, "That's him," and Freckles suddenly appeared. He was running wide open along the stone fence with his head up, and that's when my uncle told me to holler to my pet. So I did, and to my surprise, Freckles stopped dead in his tracks and looked my way. With a very slow trot, my pet ran toward me and then stopped. Freckles looked back toward the rock fence and with a snarl he reluctantly turned and walked to me.

Getting on my knees and putting my arms out, Freckles walked into them and licked my face. Hugging my dog, I turned toward my uncle and he was filled with tears of happiness. Reaching down to help me up he openly showed affection for Freckles and me.

With a soft pat on my dog's head, he said, "Let's get out of here and get Freckles home so he can cool down and get some food and water. That little hound has earned his keep today." Laughing and looking up at my uncle, there was a vivid aura that encircled this gentle man. That was the exact moment when I realized that we were a team, and the three of us had just witnessed the birth of a tradition and a bond that would never be broken. Taking our time, we walked to the old green Nash, and when uncle opened the door, he made a surprising and profound reference to the reality that it was Sunday and we had missed church, but he felt that our maker would understand and he had created foxes, hounds and children for moments like this. Not knowing what to say, Freckles said it all by jumping onto my uncle with love and affection. My uncle patted my friend and uttered that he's not only an ugly, one-eyed fox hound, but he understands loyalty and kindness.

Driving home was uneventful, since the three of us were tired. My mom and dad were waiting on the porch when we pulled into the drive, and my dad met us at the car. He offered my uncle a cold beer and told me to feed and water Freckles. He said he would have a glass of iced tea ready when I was finished. Sitting on the porch with my family, Uncle Lee and my dad discussed the day in detail. I was exhausted and needed a nap, as suggested by my mother. To be honest, I didn't wake up until she called me for school the following morning!

CHAPTER 4

The Championship

The following two weeks were uneventful except for discussion surrounding the preparation for the championship. All of those details were left up to the adults, and I must admit this was a bit unnerving to me. I could feel there was more to this championship than I was privileged to hear. I never said anything in regard to this feeling and it was obvious that in a few days my questions would be answered.

The night before the championship, our small kitchen was frantic with company. My six uncles and my dad were drinking beer and my poor mom was busy trying to make lunches and protect my sister, who was baffled and frazzled. Uncle Lee was mysteriously missing. I realized that there was a significant issue when my mom said, "Okay, you guys will have to take this outside so I can get things ready and prepare the kids for bed." My mom's assertiveness was evident, and my father knew she was all business. Needless to say, the session was over.

After the tension subsided and conversation was resumed by my parents, my mom asked Dad where Uncle Lee could be, and my dad replied, "I think I know and just let it be."

Finally, the entire formality for going to bed was over and my sister and I were tucked in. My parents both appeared to be burdened by something I obviously wasn't meant to know.

I was tired and anxious, and my sister finally broke the anxiety by saying, "Ray, try to sleep; it will be okay."

Up and eating breakfast at four o'clock, I could hear Uncle Lee on the porch, and he quietly walked into the kitchen. My mom asked if he had eaten, and he said, "No, that's why I'm early."

My mom smiled and complimented my uncle by saying, "You're clean-shaven and you look sharp this morning." My uncle thanked her and laughingly commented that he even had aftershave on! My mother laughed out loud and replied, "I know-it's Old Spice." Everyone laughed. The final preparations were finished, so it was time to leave.

While my father and uncle packed our lunches and cooler into the trunk of the old Nash, I prepared what I felt Freckles would need for the trip. I was laying an old blanket on the back floorboard, and that's when my father said he had the new chain, which went unchallenged. My mom walked slowly to the car and with some bewilderment said, "Don't you think it might be nice if you brought Freckles along for company?"

My dad howled and replied, "We thought Ray had him." Uncle Lee shook his head in disbelief and thanked her. Going to fetch Freckles, it was evident that if the rest of day was this disorganized, we were in for a long one. Freckles was stretching, and with a yawn, he walked slowly toward the Nash and looked back at me as if he needed reassurance. Sliding into the back seat, I told my pet to get in, but he turned and walked back to his water dish and tipped it over. Then he ran to the Nash and jumped inside. Uncle Lee asked if Freckles was okay and I replied that he didn't like stale water with leaves in it.

My dad kissed my mom goodbye and she opened the back door and gave me a hug. Before she closed the door, she reached down and squeezed my hand and told Freckles to watch over the three of us.

With the car started and lights turned on, Dad pulled out and headed toward our destination. Uncle Lee told me it was a one-hour drive and I should lie down and rest.

To my surprise, Freckles was already sound asleep and snoring. Dad started a conversation that was badly needed. The discussion revolved around the rules and regulations that were mandatory for determining first place in the championship. These requirements were being discussed in earnest and in my ignorance, I injected a thought. I meekly stated that it would be easier to just let the dogs decide the winner. Both my dad and uncle shut up and I knew I had hit a nerve. Uncle Lee turned around and informed me that some things should be left to kids to clarify more simply.

My father asked if Earl had entered, and my uncle's answer was uncharacteristically sharp and curt. My father said, "Sorry." That was the first indication that this was more than a fox hunt; this was personal. I wasn't comfortable with the atmosphere evident in the Nash. The silence was deafening.

I heard my uncle spit into the coffee can, and that's when he raised his voice and replied, "There's no room in this world for liars, cheats and thieves." Silence again overtook the Nash and it was so quiet that I could hear Freckles breathing. Lying down on the seat, I reached for my pet for comfort. I was discouraged, and Freckles seemed to understand this, and put his head on the arm I dangled in his direction. There was obviously tension mounting, and that's when my uncle told my father to pull into the next gas station. Daylight hadn't broken yet, and there was very little traffic. My dad appeared nervous and rushed. Pulling into the station, my father informed my uncle that if the gas gauge worked, the car was full. The atmosphere was tense, and that's when Uncle Lee said, "Stop the damn car," and my dad obeyed. Observing my dad obeying his order was similar to my reaction when Dad gave me such direction.

Uncle Lee told me to sit up and listen. "This needs to be said. Everyone is speculating on my motive, so let's clear the air. This isn't about me, it's about principle, and its time for both of you to understand that regardless of the result, you and Freckles deserve this opportunity." With Freckles sitting next to me, it was evident that he sensed tension and somehow understood that this minor confrontation was about him. Uncle Lee told my dad to turn around and a question was directed toward me. "Ray, if you feel you and Freckles would rather not make this attempt, that's no problem. How do you feel about continuing with the objective?"

My father stated that I didn't understand, and that's when Uncle Lee turned toward my dog and calmly said, "They both understand; it's you that has confused the issue with your lack of confidence." I felt that there was only one choice, and I said, "We're a team, and Freckles is the captain, so how much further is the drive?"

My dad started the car and asked me, "Do we turn left or right?"

I said, "This is right, so turn toward the competition." The conversation was somewhat strained, yet my uncle reinforced my choice by explaining carefully what I should expect upon arrival and the procedure that would be involved with registering Freckles.

Daybreak was struggling and the fall colors were gorgeous. The red and yellow hues stood out against the light of breaking day. My father informed me that we were only a mile from the entry to the rod and gun club where this event was taking place. I remember thinking that with all the confusion and nervousness, it was going to be exciting and enjoyable, regardless of the outcome. My uncle gave instructions to Dad suggesting where we should park. I knew then that my uncle had scouted this area and probably spent quite a bit of time thinking about this championship.

Making a left turn onto a dirt road, I could see taillights moving slowly ahead of us. As we followed several trucks with dog cages inside, my uncle told me that there would be several different types of hounds entered. I inquired as to what type of hounds, and he replied by naming black and tans, redbones, walkers, German shorthairs and blueticks. All of a sudden, the dirt road opened up; I hadn't expected so much traffic and confusion. People were scurrying about and several men armed with flashlights attempted to park the vehicles that were primarily trucks; new trucks at that. My uncle said, "There will be four or five hundred people here, so stay close to your father and me." It was then that I asked what about Freckles. He said, "Just leave him in the car for now. It will be okay." There was hollering and directions were being given over a megaphone. I laughed out loud when Freckles seemed to shake his head in bewilderment. We both saw the excitement that was evident in the mass confusion.

Parking the Nash, the three of us slowly got out and I saw my uncle remove his chew, take off his cap throw it into the car. He raised his hand and attempted to arrange his thinning hair properly. Taking my hand, my father told me not to react to any conversation that might take place. He suggested I just stay close to him or Uncle Lee. The three of us started walking slowly toward the clubhouse, which was surrounded by clusters of people that were frantic in an attempt to keep things organized. My uncle slowed down and waited for me. He reached down and took my hand. I could feel all of the anxiety leave my body and it was replaced with a sense of security. I couldn't help noticing that my dad was walking with a swagger that I had only seen on occasion.

There was an atmosphere present that is difficult to describe. Hounds were barking, men were yelling and it was like a switch went on when I heard, "Leon Richards is here." A mysterious silence was evident as the three of us reached the steps that took us inside a huge room with tables set up and men standing in line signing and dropping off papers.

The hubbub was subdued as my uncle slowly walked toward the shortest line. He leaned down and whispered in my ear, "Ray, this won't take long, so try to relax."

It was obvious that every person in the huge room was watching my uncle, Dad and I. Several people acknowledged us and said hello. A few asked if we had entered, and my uncle graciously said hello, but nothing more. A man ahead of us in line turned around and reached out his hand to my uncle and they shook. The tall, slim man smiled at me and asked why we were there. Uncle Lee replied that it was a beautiful day and his nephew was interested in this event. Uncle Lee squeezed my hand and chuckled. When it was our turn to register, he reached into his jacket pocket, handed me the envelope and whispered, "Everything you need is in here, so just hand it to the gentleman."

The guy behind the table said, "Hello Leon, what can I do for you?"

Uncle Lee replied, "I don't need anything, but Ray has the paperwork for his hound." The reaction from the man handling this process was strange at best. Taking the envelope that I handed him, it was obvious that he was baffled and guarded. Opening the envelope and reading the paper filled out by my uncle, he slowly put the paper on the table and peered over his glasses. He informed us that some of the questions weren't answered. Uncle Lee stated, "It's all there, so what's the problem?"

"Well, first off, the hound's history is missing and the pedigree papers aren't included," he said. In a very assertive voice my uncle told the man to direct all the questions regarding the dog to his owner.

Looking at me with a grin, Uncle Lee said, "Ray, answer his questions the best way you know how."

With some reluctance, I replied, "That's fine." I turned and I saw my dad standing alone, sipping a cup of black coffee. He smiled and nodded his head with approval. Obviously, this was going to be a moment that defined our team.

The entire room was silent and the man said, "I'm not sure I can do that, because the owner is only eleven and the dog has no pedigree."

Uncle Lee stood straight and tall and told the man to address the damn questions to his nephew, who was more than capable of responding to any inquiry pertaining to his hound. Uncle Lee continued, "The only problem is your insecurity in accepting my nephew's capability." The man was intimidated by my uncle's assertiveness and slowly stood up and informed my uncle that he didn't have the authority to approve our entry. That was when my Uncle Lee reached out and put both hands on the table. He looked up at this nervous man and I started fidgeting and was totally nervous as Uncle Lee raised his voice with conviction and replied, "Go find the president for resolution of this conflict." I wasn't aware that my dad had stepped behind me and Uncle Lee for moral support. Dad reached out and rustled my hair to reassure me. I needed it.

The man in charge of our registration yelled, "Somebody go find Martha."

Uncle Lee softly replied, "That's smart of you, since you're not capable of making a simple decision on your own."

The man said, "Leon, we've been friends for years."

But that statement was abruptly interrupted by my uncle as he held up his hand and replied, "You don't know what a friend is. Don't insult my nephew." Man, things were getting tense and heated.

The silence in the huge room was unsettling and I noticed that others were looking over with concern and intrigue. My uncle replied loud enough for everyone to hear, "If this issue isn't resolved quickly, it will be uncomfortable for everyone concerned."

It was then that my uncle turned and asked my dad to go get Freckles, and my dad replied, "Okay, that's a smart decision," and quickly left. Uncle Lee looked at his pocket watch and informed the crowd that their hounds would be turned loose in 45 minutes.

Someone hollered, "That's okay, Leon, this is more interesting than any hunt."

My uncle replied, "This has been a long time coming."

Suddenly, a door in the back of the room opened, and that's when the atmosphere changed immediately. A lady walked through the door of the room. She had long snow white hair that shined like her diamond earrings. Her hair was piled up on top of her head, giving her height. She was wearing a red fox jacket that fit snugly at the waist, and it was accented with a high collar that hugged her cheeks. She wore black slacks and high heel boots trimmed with fox fur. Her white turtleneck sweater was accented with red beads. For the first time in my life, I was astounded by a woman's beauty. Her eyes were dark blue, and sparkled like sapphires. This lady walked slowly toward us with grace and confidence, reached out her hand toward my uncle and he took it comfortably.

She said, "Hello Leon," and asked him if this young man was Ray.

My uncle replied, "Yes Martha, this is my nephew."

She knelt down and grabbed my hand and asked me if Freckles was there. I responded, "Yes ma'am."

She followed that up with, "How old is Freckles?" I responded, "around four years old," and then she asked what kind of foxhound Freckles was. I told her that my Uncle Lee said he was walker and bluetick. She smiled and leaned closer, and I became aware of her perfume. I realized that I was comfortable with this lady. She slowly stood up, still holding my hand as she graciously reached out with her other hand for my uncle. Looking into my uncle's eyes, she turned toward everyone and very calmly replied that Freckles was entered. If anyone objected, they would have to submit the paperwork within the next 30 seconds. This lady squeezed my hand casually and kissed my uncle on the cheek, and he appeared pleased.

My dad walked into the hall with Freckles, and as soon as my pet saw me, he walked slowly toward me, Martha and Uncle Lee. Martha laughed out loud, turned toward my uncle and said, "He is blind in one eye, bow-legged and ugly, yet he's gorgeous."

This lady reached down, patted Freckles and took my hand, stating, "This dog loves you, Ray, and it shows. I have work to do, so let's get the show on the road."

My uncle said, "Martha, thank you," and she winked.

Then she said, "We will all thank each other later."

The judges had been placed in their areas of responsibility and the hound owners and dogs were lined up ready to be released. The excitement was building. The team walked slowly toward the starting position where hounds were leashed and howling with excitement. Freckles was a bit nervous due to the commotion and he walked between Uncle Lee and me for guidance. A man with a megaphone started counting down from thirty and Uncle Lee said with conviction, "Ray, watch carefully and remember what is going to take place."

When the countdown was finished and the hounds were released, I marveled at how the pack started working the area where one of the tagged foxes had been released that morning. It seemed evident that most of the hounds were followers, but a few were somewhat independent. Freckles was still sitting next to me and he appeared somewhat nervous. It was Uncle Lee who said casually, "Well that's that." I looked up at my uncle with confusion and bewilderment. I didn't know what was going to transpire next, and that's when Uncle Lee told me to give Freckles his hunting direction.

I stated abruptly, "How in the world do you expect Freckles to compete against what we just observed?"

My dad walked to my side and replied, "Ray, this is no time to question your hound and Uncle Lee's expertise."

For the first time, I was somewhat assertive with Dad and Uncle Lee. I slowly uttered, "Freckles won't hunt under these conditions. This doesn't make any sense."

I expected some problem with my attitude, and that's when Uncle Lee stepped in and said, "Trust me and just tell Freckles to get on with it. You'll understand in a few minutes." Reluctantly, I stood and prepared to instruct Freckles to start hunting. My pet instinctively knew what was taking place and he appeared confident. I just pointed and told him to go get some foxes. It was then when Freckles looked up at me with his one eye. With his tail standing straight up, he turned in the opposite direction that the other hounds had taken. By the time he hit the field, he was behind all the spectators, whom he ignored. Freckles was wide open and all business. It was obvious that he understood the process even better than I had hoped.

My father's back was turned, so I grabbed his belt to get his attention. When he turned to acknowledge me, I grappled with an attempt to apologize. He simply nodded his head in understanding. I couldn't help noticing that a very fat man was approaching my uncle. This man was chewing on a cigar, and I realized his jacket was three or four sizes too small. His belly hung over his belt and I laughed to myself, thinking that his pants would fall down with one hearty sneeze. His face was puffy and red. His suede jacket and boots were matching. This man's face had a scowl that appeared to be permanent. Uncle Lee stepped beside me and informed me not to respond to any conversation unless I felt uncomfortable.

This arrogant-appearing man walked directly to me and without any hesitation, asked what business I had entering this hunt. I just stood there bewildered as two more questions were fired in my direction. These questions were extremely hurtful and degrading. He asked, "Do you think that mutt of yours has a chance against my hounds?" He also wanted to know why I didn't have a real hound. Both my dad and uncle were physically tense, and that's when I angrily asked a question of my own.

I was surprisingly assertive when I said, "Who wants to know?" My father laughed and Uncle Lee took both hands and placed them on my shoulders. Uncle Lee told me not to get too close to Earl, because he didn't want the smell to rub off.

With confidence and satisfaction, Uncle Lee directed a statement to Fat Earl. "Earl, have you lost weight?"

Then my uncle asked another question that perplexed me. "Have you shot any hounds lately?" The air was still like the personality of most of the spectators who were watching this impromptu conversation. Earl's face got redder and he appeared extremely agitated. Then my Dad broke the tension by saying it's time to get some fresh air. Uncle Lee smiled and told Earl it would help if he took some laxatives and the three of us walked toward the Nash. This experience was more than I had bargained for, but in spite of all the confusion and confrontation, I felt I had acquired a swagger of my own.

Walking through the crowd of onlookers, the three of us knew that Freckles had allowed us an opportunity to share love, tolerance and growth, each in our own way. Looking back, it was a magical time as I walked in front with Dad behind me, and that rustic old man was behind it all. Uncle Lee stopped occasionally to visit with some friends and supporters. As luck would have it, a bark off in the distance stood out and the hair on the back of my neck stood up. When I turned to share the news, both my dad and uncle were high-fiving long before it was popular. Finally, we reached the old Nash to eat lunch and regroup. My uncle appeared to have been transformed into a much younger and vibrant man. The pitfalls of life that burdened him throughout his existence had suddenly vanished. He smiled with renewed understanding coupled with enthusiasm. My dad turned, reached out and hugged Uncle Lee. I heard him say, "Thank you." There was love, respect and vigor for life that three generations were openly sharing.

During the lunch prepared by Mom, I remember having my typical peanut butter and jam sandwich with a Hostess cupcake for dessert and the usual apple that mom always insisted on. Dad had ham and cheese, while Uncle Lee munched on a bologna sandwich. We all had cold root beer. There was a sense of peace and contentment. This emotional lunch was interrupted by Uncle Lee informing us of the plan for the remainder of the hunt. He told my dad to drive him to the old wooden bridge and drop the two of us off. Dad was instructed to cruise around and periodically check the results coming into the clubhouse. My dad drove the Nash to the bridge and got out and looked around for a comfortable place to sit and listen for the music of the hounds. Dad pulled away and waved. My uncle and I stood on the old wooden bridge, looked into the cold, clear stream, and we started a conversation about fishing, trapping and hunting. It was obvious even for an eleven-year-old that my uncle was a bit melancholy and wanted to talk.

As I asked him a simple question, he shuffled with unexpected emotion. The question was, "How do you feel about your life, and have you been happy?"

He said, "Let's sit down and while we're listening for Freckles, we'll talk." Sitting down on some soft green and grey moss of the forest floor, my uncle decided to sit on a stump that seemed to fit. I was all ears when he told me that perhaps it was time to have this talk, because there may never be a chance again. He started at the beginning. Apparently, it all started for him in his youth, which had been filled with nature, sports and work, in that order. It had been happy and rewarding. He glowed with satisfaction as he explained that he had worked as a welder at the plant and decided to quit because it was confining. Foxhounds had been a passion that provided a good income after selling the fox pelts and some trained hounds. "Your dad's father died unexpectedly and had left ten children that needed male guidance," he said. "He had felt it was up to him to assist his sister, who was my grandmother, in her attempt to raise three girls and seven boys with no income. He had always raised hounds, which he sold for extra money on occasion. This passion had enabled him to learn and develop techniques for training hounds and he admitted having some dandies.

I interrupted his story to ask why he never married. Looking down at the moss, he simply said it wasn't in the cards. He felt raising ten kids was the priority and he had no regrets. He continued that as he got older and looking back, he had made difficult decisions that couldn't be changed. I must admit that this conversation was murky at best for my age; however, I remember details to this day. Uncle Lee looked into my eyes and with passion told me to listen carefully. "There will be times in your life when it's difficult, but always remember that honesty and integrity are developed and absolutely essential in life's pursuits," he said. "It will always win in the end. Try to treat people with respect and kindness. It always feels good." Uncle Lee said he was proud of my ability to handle the conversation with Fat Earl. He told me to pick and choose my battles and never get into a pissing match with a skunk.

Trying to digest all of this information was like memorizing my spelling assignments at school. Spelling wasn't my strong suit then or now. My uncle raised his head to listen for the hounds and asked if I had heard Freckles. I shook my head yes and said, "He's alone."

Uncle Lee smiled and replied, "I know." Since the subject was back to the task at hand, I inquired about the judging of the hounds and delicately asked why fat Earl appeared angry and didn't like Freckles.

"Well Ray, this area has several acres of land surrounded by water. Dirt roads circle the entire area. This makes it possible for the judges to observe the foxes and hounds as they run across the roads. They account for the first three hounds chasing the tagged fox, and depending on placement, the hounds win points," he said. "Did you notice that the hounds that looked alike had color ribbons?"

I replied "yes."

"That gives each hound a fair evaluation as fair as possible," he said. I asked how many foxes had been released, and he answered, "Five foxes are released, and four of them are located randomly throughout the area a day before the hunt. One fox is released near the starting line four hours before releasing the hounds. Each fox is tagged in the ear with a colored ribbon for identification. There are four judges at each location, and every time a fox crosses the road, the fox is identified. The hounds are also identified when they cross the road in pursuit. One judge is responsible for the fox and the other three judges are assigned to hound placement, one, two and three. Points are tallied appropriately. It's not an exact science, but it works. The hounds will be allowed three hours of pursuit, and then the final two hours are when the foxes are shot and higher points are awarded to a hound placement when they get to the downed fox. I know it seems complicated, but don't worry, Freckles will fare well. The hunt is over after all the foxes have been dispatched or after five hours are up; whichever comes first. This location was designed because it's surrounded by water. Foxes don't like water, so they usually don't escape."

With confusion showing on my face, Uncle Lee stood up, stretched and referred to the reality that he was getting older by the minute.

Reluctantly, I asked what Earl's problem with Freckles was. Uncle Lee laughed and said that Freckles was a serious threat and Earl knew it. "Ray, for many years that I hate to count I've been involved with foxhounds and my reputation within the foxhound association is honorable," he said. "Most of the members are friends of mine. Understand that Earl has a huge foxhound kennel and raises pedigree redbones and black and tans. He always viewed me as a threat because my hounds were formidable competition against his business. His problem seemed to revolve around money and nothing more. There were years when I never entered this hunt because it wasn't necessary for my hounds to have those types of credentials. Everyone knew the quality of my hounds and it spoke volumes within the hound community. Over seven years ago, I had a walker that was perhaps the best hound I ever trained. Her name was Martha. She was named after her owner. That dog had characteristics similar to Freckles. I knew she would probably win this championship, so for the hell of it I entered her. Times were tough and money was scarce and Earl hated competition, since his kennel needed money and recognition. During the hunt it became evident that Martha was heads above the other hounds and was about to humiliate Earl's entry. During the time when the foxes were being shot, Martha came up missing. I suspected the worst and I found her shot and in the area where Earl had been assigned to judge. I know he shot her, and to be honest, that bastard enjoyed my grief. Ever since that day I never attended any meetings and didn't want anything to do with this championship. Money can bring the worst out in people."

I interrupted my uncle and asked three questions that I needed clarified. The first question was, "Is it the same Martha?" The second question was, "Was it difficult to walk away from your love and passion for hounds?" The last and most significant question was difficult for me to ask, but I knew I deserved to know the truth. "Why Freckles and me?" I was sorry I asked the last question because Uncle Lee sat down on the stump, put his head down and put his hands over his face and wept openly. Watching my uncle cry with sobs I went to him and put my arms around this old rustic man who loved unconditionally and had sacrificed his entire life for his family. There were emotions that were surfacing within us that words cannot describe. It would be fruitless to attempt. There is one word that would describe this moment and that is love.

When Uncle Lee wiped his eyes he seemed suddenly frail and vulnerable. At that moment, I realized that my uncle had sensitivity toward life that never showed because of his pride and dignity, and that was sad in itself. Watching down the road, I could see the green Nash coming to pick us up. After getting in and heading toward the clubhouse, my father informed us that there were three hounds in contention. One of the hounds belonged to Earl the other two belonged to Eddie and me. My excitement was internal and Uncle Lee stated that Eddie always had good hounds that were well taken care of. As we drove up to the clubhouse, there seemed to be confusion evident on the steps and also inside the hall. After parking and getting out of the Nash, a man approached us. He appeared concerned about something significant and he walked toward me and asked my father if he could talk to me personally. Dad said okay.

The man was polite and told me that Earl had filed papers to protest Freckles' entry. With a jolt, my Uncle Lee softly said, "Tell us something we didn't expect."

The man said, "I'm sorry; Ray, but this will complicate the final decision." I looked toward Dad and Uncle Lee and said, "Take me to Earl."

Dad said, "I'm not sure that's a good idea."

Uncle Lee interrupted and replied, "It's time for Earl to meet the owner of this hound."

Dad flinched and rubbed his chin in thought. He turned to me and gave me one instruction. "Remember who you represent and make us proud."

I whispered to my uncle, "Don't get into a pissing match with a skunk." He winked. I realized at eleven years old that during the past few weeks I had gained confidence and an honest understanding of the value for standing up for what's right. I started toward the clubhouse and when I got to the steps I asked everyone, "Where's Fat Earl?" To my surprise, Earl walked around the corner and as it was obvious I was standing alone, I wondered if my decision was wise. I remembered my uncle's emotional pain that this man had intentionally caused. I looked up and politely asked why he had formally protested against Freckles. He grunted an answer that was technically above my ability to comprehend, which really didn't bother me. With a sense of purpose, I simply responded with, "You have good dogs, so why are you afraid of Freckles?"

Taking the smelly chewed cigar out of his mouth he snickered, "I'm not afraid of your mutt. That mutt of yours doesn't belong with these pedigree hounds and it will diminish the credentials of this hunt. Take your mutt and go back to where you belong." Everyone was aghast at his ignorance and arrogance. I felt support from the adults, which helped my nervousness.

Putting my head down with the appearance of defeat, I suddenly looked up with confidence and replied, "If this damn hunt is that important to your business, I have two dollars in the bank and I'll send it to you." Everyone laughed.

Fat Earl got really red-faced and replied, "I don't need your money."

I shrugged my shoulders with confusion and said, "I can solve this issue in one of two ways. I can withdraw Freckles, which you'd like, or you could shoot him. Regardless of any decision, my mutt Freckles will finish this hunt on all four legs. My dad and uncle never quit and you're not going to scare me with your threats."

When the crowd heard that remark, I overheard a man utter, "He's a chip off the old block."

I turned and said, "The hounds will settle this problem, regardless of any decision about Freckles."

Fat Earl was really upset and stated, "No snot-nosed kid and his mutt are going to humiliate or threaten me."

I looked around and simply said, "I didn't have to. You already smell like a skunk, and Uncle Lee told me to never get into a pissing match with a fat skunk."

Everyone in the hall got really quiet and I walked to my dad and uncle. When I got nearer, they both grabbed me and held me close. Dad hugged me long and hard, then Uncle Lee stated, "He's a one-eyed bow-legged foxhound, but he may be the best damn hound found any where in the whole state.

It came to our attention that four of the foxes had been shot and the last fox with the red tag, which hadn't been spotted, was still out there. Everyone was convinced that he had swum the river. The results were being calculated and Dad told me that Freckles was missing and two other hounds hadn't been located and everyone seemed concerned. I asked my dad if he heard him and he said no.

I asked about how much time before it was over. Dad replied thirty-five minutes. Uncle Lee told my father to drive to the wooden bridge and put the blanket and my jacket down for Freckles to find. I was scared as hell and everyone was buzzing with anticipation. Uncle Lee and I walked to the board and I could see from the standings that Earl's dog was tied with Freckles and Eddie's dog was third.

I was tired, upset and determined all at the same time. Uncle Lee leaned down and thanked me and I replied, "Right is right and you showed me that." With a renewed understanding about values that had been pounded into my head I wondered why people went to such extremes over a fox hunt. I remember asking Uncle Lee that question and he simply stated that when I got older, life would be filled with people like Earl. With sincerity, I said, "There's no room for liars, cheats and thieves." Uncle Lee apologized for the difficulty this hunt had caused, and with respect and a new understanding I replied, "Let the hounds decide the results."

He answered, "That's absolutely correct. You're old beyond your years Ray, and you have a lifetime to enjoy foxes and the values that are acquired developing respect for nature."

All of a sudden, Martha came out of the office and walked toward me. She had tears in her eyes and Uncle Lee was obviously upset. Her grace and beauty were still evident, yet she looked at my uncle and told him that he had made the right decision and the result was clear. I noticed that my uncle's chin was quivering from emotion. I heard her tell my uncle that she had resigned her position immediately after Earl filed his complaint. "Times have changed and its time to start over," she said. He nodded in agreement.

Uncle Lee talked to Martha and I was concern about Freckles, since the other hounds had been found.

Looking around for Earl, I saw him talking to a few people and he was very upset. There were only a few minutes left and my concern was for my pet. Martha was standing next to me and softly replied that Freckles was part walker from the hound that Earl may have shot. "Your uncle and I were devastated; however, we didn't have the proof," she said. I told her that if that was true, that part of her hound was still out there. She looked into my eyes and said that she felt the hunt had been decided and Earl would be awarded the winner. Then the Nash pulled in and Dad jumped out of the car seeming tired and worried.

The judges were gathered around the porch with three trophies and Fat Earl was up front. He was ready to make a speech and accept his trophy. The judges looked at their watches and felt that there was no need to wait any longer and everyone agreed with applause. With my head down, Martha put her arm around me and told me to look up. She yelled, "That ugly, one-eyed hound is coming from behind the clubhouse dragging that red-tagged fox." Both Freckles and the fox were soaking wet and I started to cry. The tears were contagious as my dad and Uncle Lee dropped their heads in disbelief. Freckles dragged the fox in front of the porch and dropped it at Earl's feet, and then ran to me. With an expression of excitement, Freckles was happy and surprisingly playful. No one said a word as they stared in disbelief. Then my uncle walked up to me, knelt down and kissed me on the forehead. Gently removing his cap, he gave Martha a kiss and they hugged with affection. My dad was beside himself as he reached down and put me on his shoulders. He walked toward the porch and then stopped and returned to his place alongside his uncle. After receiving congratulations from friends, I looked for Freckles and noticed him trotting out back of the clubhouse. When he returned, he had another dead fox in his mouth, which he also dropped at the feet of Fat Earl. Now it was Freckles who appeared to have a bit of a swagger.

It goes without saying that Freckles had hunted down that tagged fox and killed it. He also must have smelled out another fox that resided in the area. There was confusion that surrounded these events, but no one knows for sure. Uncle Lee had seen Freckles run down a fox in the past, but never two.

The judges had no choice but to award Freckles the winner. When they called my name to accept the trophy, I graciously accepted. Going down the stairs to join my family, I put the trophy at Earl's feet. I must give him credit for staying around to witness his defeat.

After visiting with the spectators and finally getting into the old Nash, all of us were exhausted and it showed. As my dad drove down the dirt road, it was obvious Martha was following. Uncle Lee openly informed Dad and me that even after winning the hunt it was important to move on.

Freckles was exhausted and slept peacefully at my feet. My father asked me if this hunt was what I had expected and I replied, "Not really." Uncle Lee explained that if nothing else was accomplished, the one-eyed, bow-legged hound was the best hound in the hunt! Then he surprisingly stated that somewhere there was a hound in the state that was perhaps better. He laughed and informed me that we had proven our point, which made it worth the effort.

Slipping into sleep, I remember hearing, "Well, hockey season is just around the corner." The trapping season was about to open in a week and whitetail hunting, which was an obsession in our family, would start getting some serious priority.

I fell asleep on the back seat until my mom woke me. She gave me a hug with happiness. My sister was glad we won and wondered where we put the foxes. It was starting to get dark and the leaves were falling off the old oak. That meant there were leaves to rake into piles for distribution into the garden. Sitting on the porch enjoying my family, I noticed Martha's car pulling into the drive. She was met by my uncle, and I could tell he was extremely pleased to see her.

Martha reached into her car for her purse and she also pulled out the trophy.

Raising the trophy, my uncle kissed her on the cheek. My mom and dad were visibly affected.

As I fed and watered Freckles, it was obvious that he had enough for one day. He walked into his doghouse and laid down, appearing satisfied. There was no question that he had earned his keep.

Joining my family sitting on the porch, we had one new member. It was being discussed openly that perhaps it was time to put all things in the past and walk into the future with renewed optimism. The conversation was not relevant to me, but I knew everyone was pleased and satisfied.

During the conversation about the events of the hunt, I was surprised to hear the accounts by my dad and uncle. Each of us obviously had different versions to share regarding specific details. Even at my young age, I wondered if I had attended the same hunt.

CHAPTER 5

Introduction to the Trap Line

My mother turned in my direction and informed me that the Christmas catalog had arrived and the Red Rider BB gun was pictured on the inside cover. It was then that Uncle Lee asked her if I had permission to get involved with his trap line this coming Saturday. "If you're willing to wake him before daylight and feed him breakfast it's okay," She replied, and said it was also his responsibility to raise my spelling grade. That was a serious matter in our family. He told my mother that he couldn't spell either and she told him that it was time to learn. No one laughed and he appeared somewhat reluctant. The other condition was that I was to share in the profits. Uncle Lee wasn't comfortable with these demands, yet he agreed.

Martha injected some ideas about spelling and it was clear she was on Mom's side. Then she informed me that she was a fifth grade teacher, but I was still fond of her.

Then it was time to eat the venison stew with the typical hot homemade bread and no one objected.

The conversation was geared toward trapping muskrats, mink, coons, beaver and foxes. Uncle Lee reminded everyone that my issue with picking my fingers with a wire brush was going to be rewarded. Dad openly suggested that tomorrow morning would be a great time to scout the trap line. Or, on second thought, maybe it would be smarter to leave around noon. Everyone agreed that sleep was badly needed after the emotional day.

It goes without saying that the victory didn't go unnoticed. The phone rang off the hook and my father's brothers started showing up with congratulations. To be honest, I was ready for bed and looked forward to help Uncle Lee finish boiling traps for the coming weekend.

My mom and dad allowed me the luxury of sleeping in Sunday morning and missing church. That was great, because it allowed me to join Uncle Lee in his trapper's shed. Running into the shed, I was greeted with a smile that beamed with satisfaction. The potbelly stove was burning and the trap dye was simmering, ready for a dozen or so number one rat traps.

Placing the traps into the pail, Uncle Lee informed me that my spelling issue was up to me since he couldn't be helpful. The conversation about schoolwork was brief, but direct. "Ray, you need to spend quality time on your schoolwork, and if you don't, your mom will enforce her authority," he said. I knew that already and promised to concentrate on my studies.

The atmosphere was a bit subdued because we were emotionally drained from the hunt. Freckles had been wandering around the shed since Uncle Lee had released him to help limber his joints. It was evident that Uncle Lee was more than impressed with his performance when he referred to him catching and killing two foxes at the same hunt. He told me that he had never heard or seen anything like that from a hound.

The day was filled with company and reliving the hunt, and finally, Uncle Lee said ,"I'm tired of the discussion. Go tell your mom or dad we're heading for the beaver pond and the two creeks above Tyos farm." My parents said okay if Uncle Lee supplied lunch. I was instructed to be home for supper. It was always at five o'clock p.m. on Sundays.

As the two of us got into the Nash, Freckles appeared and Uncle Lee got out and let him into the back seat. Heading down the road, he informed me that Freckles was deserving of spending the day with us. I thought that was kind and nice. As he took a chunk of Yankee Girl and manipulated it in his cheek, I was informed that trapping would allow me freedom to understand nature and wildlife in a way that can't be taught in any school. He was very serious and said that I was to listen and ask questions if I didn't understand what he was going to explain.

Driving through the countryside, autumn had taken over and it was beyond explanation. My uncle expressed that he had always wanted to paint, but never tried. He awkwardly confessed to pencil sketches which he would show me when the time was right. I was amazed and had difficulty comprehending that statement.

As he pulled into a farm drive, we were greeted by the owner of the farm. Uncle Lee and Clayton were friends from childhood, and the conversation was cheerful and relaxed. Uncle Lee introduced me and told Clayton, the farmer, that we were headed for the beaver pond. Clayton told us that there were several beavers working the lower end of the last meadow. Uncle Lee thanked him and told him they would be gone in two weeks. The farmer told me to learn all I could, since my uncle was the best trapper he knew. I was surprised, but thankful to be in this old man's company.

As we drove through the meadows and harvested cornfields, the world that I was about to enter officially seemed magical and mysterious. Putting the brakes on, he pointed toward a sandpit about the size of a small garage. He told me not to let Freckles out because he could see a fresh fox track in the sand. The two of us got out and slowly walked toward the sand. My uncle walked with his head down and then stopped dead in his tracks. He gently grabbed my arm and told me to remember this instruction, there in the sand were tracks that appeared to be dog-like, but they were narrow and more pointed. He told me to follow the track with my eyes and tell him what I saw. The only obvious observation was that it appeared that the animal only had two legs. "That's right," he said. "However, I won't show or explain why these tracks look the way they do because we don't have time."

He then told me to look closely at the track below our feet and asked me to describe it. The track was more pointed than a dog track, about the size of a large cat. The toes appeared to have three long nails and the fox didn't appear to be running. Uncle Lee rubbed my head with approval and said, "You're better at understanding fox tracks than most of your uncles, but don't tell them I said that."

Walking back toward the Nash, it was evident that Freckles was asleep and it was then that Uncle Lee told me that we would catch one or two foxes in that sand. That sounded exciting to me and the trapping addiction was slowly seeping into my blood. The air was still, cool and invigorating, which we both seemed to enjoy.

The weather had been warmer than normal and my uncle made reference to the fur-bearers needing cooler temperatures to put on their guard hairs. I asked what guard hairs were and his answer was that he'd show me later. Getting into the Nash, we headed toward the beaver pond, and that's when my uncle said, "Damn! These beavers are raising hell on Clayton's property. We need to clean them out before they do any more damage." It was neat for my uncle to include me in this venture.

It was the first time I was aware of the peace and solitude of a beaver pond. The fall colors were reflecting back onto the still water and it reminded me of a mirror image. My uncle wandered slowly toward the pond and he also made reference to the majestic beauty. Two wood ducks flushed, which startled us, and we laughed. "Let's sit down and enjoy the view," he said, and we found suitable sitting arrangements. Freckles was walking beside me. Thinking back, it was a picture-perfect day.

Uncle Lee started reminiscing about his youth with feelings of longing. He recalled spending most of his free time in the wilderness. He said it was peaceful and he liked the solitude. The mysteries of nature and wildlife always intrigued him. He always respected wildlife's right to exist and that harvesting game was necessary to protect the balance, but also felt that greed was going to damage the environment. Thinking back to those days, he was correct. This conversation was filled with truth and humility and thinking back fondly, his basic personality was overwhelmed with these virtues. The relaxed atmosphere of this conversation was remarkable since very little discussion was taking place about technical details necessary for success on a trap line. I know now that the objective for this trip was to let Clayton know the beaver would be targeted. My uncle informed me that details regarding sets for animals would take place during the season and it would be easier to learn by doing.

I understood, and regardless of his purpose for this trip, I was absorbed in the placid and simple gesture of spending quality time with a rustic old man who was willing to hand off his legacy. I was grateful for the opportunity to learn and experience part of my uncle's lifestyle. Just sitting and enjoying the calm and relaxed feeling that only nature can provide, there was little conversation, and I knew instantly that my uncle was engrossed in memories of his life. Don't ask how I knew, but somehow the time was perfect for such reflection. Uncle Lee slowly stood and told me to fetch a brightly colored stick from the water, and I obeyed his request. The stick was completely void of bark and each end was pointed, as if cut with a hatchet or jack knife. Handing him the stick, he informed me that beaver had chewed off the bark and that they were primarily bark eaters, which explained the fallen trees and short stumps with sharp points. He told me that beaver loved poplar trees and fruit trees for their survival. As I digested that information, he handed me that stick, which I kept for over thirty years.

Heading back toward town, my uncle stated that he needed to stop at his liquor store for some paperwork that needed attention. Since the last few days had been emotionally draining, it was evident that Uncle Lee was tired and seemed calmer than normal. He appeared to be deep in thought, but he never mentioned clues to his pensiveness. Pulling the Nash into his parking space near the liquor store, he slowly got out and searched for his keys. He told me that he'd be right back, and it was then he offered an explanation regarding me not being allowed into the store. My parents had objected to my hanging around a liquor store, but things were changing rapidly. After returning to the car, my uncle made me an offer I couldn't refuse. Looking at his pocket watch and checking his change, he felt that we would enjoy an ice cream root beer float. That was only going to happen if I kept it between us, since supper time was only three hours away. My lips were sealed. I had my float and Uncle Lee enjoyed a cup of black coffee.

After our treat, we pulled into Dad's drive and my mom was sitting on the porch. Uncle Lee surprised me by getting out and approaching her with a question that was somewhat controversial. In his soft, gentle voice, he asked if it would be okay for my dad to bring me to the store in the evening to join his cronies that gathered every evening in the store's office area for conversation regarding endless pursuits in the wilderness. To my surprise, my mom said, "Leon, your relationship with Ray would not be complete without that experience. If his schoolwork and chores are finished, he can drop in with his dad on occasion." My uncle beamed with satisfaction, which was at the time somewhat confusing. I was excited, yet I wasn't sure why.

Letting Freckles out of the Nash, I was reminded that it was time to work on my spelling lesson that Martha had left. I wasn't happy, but knew enough not to object, knowing my limits. Uncle Lee said, "Thank you," and left for home and probably a well-deserved nap before supper.

CHAPTER 6

New Experiences and New Friends

Getting home from school and diligently doing chores and some homework, I was wondering if my dad would make a trip after supper to the liquor store, but I knew enough not to ask. I had learned to leave those decisions to my parents. It was a rainy, drab day and the wind was strong, blowing leaves off the trees, which would make raking difficult and dirty. After eating supper and helping carry dishes to the sink, my dad asked if the dogs had been attended to. I said yes and he said, "That's important, and try not to forget that they need and deserve attention." As my dad sat and relaxed with the newspaper and listened to the radio, my curiosity got the better of me, but I was saved by my mom's suggestion that it would help if Dad picked up some soap for her laundry. My father got up and started putting on his coat, and he noticed that I was standing in anticipation. He then he suggested that I wear a rain jacket and my new rubber packs if I expected to join him.

My conversation with Dad was minimal, yet informative. He tried to describe what I might encounter at Uncle Lee's store, but no warning could have prepared me for this experience. After picking up my mom's items, we headed to the store. Walking down the sidewalk next to my dad I felt safe, but a bit nervous.

The door to the liquor store was heavy and the door's window was covered with metal bars for security reasons. I needed help from Dad to open it. As the door opened, I heard bells ring and I could smell Cherry Blend, Carter Hall and Prince Albert pipe tobacco that was always present in this small enclosure. There were shelves filled with liquor bottles that were neatly lined up and lint-free. The floor was clean and waxed, and tracks caused from the rain had been mopped.

Walking slowly toward the so-called "office," I heard laughter and some chatter that sounded cheerful. My father guided me gently forward until my uncle suddenly realized our presence. Walking deliberately into this office space, it became evident it was nothing but a hunter's paradise. A huge rack buck mount was being used as a hat stand and other deer horns were hanging all over the walls. Each set of horns was at least six points and had names attached and the date. I was greeted by four old codgers the age of my uncle. They all stood up to shake the hand of the owner of the hound that won the state championship as I was welcomed into this fraternity of wise and likeable men. My uncle formally introduced me to Weasel, Mutt, Leo and Simple Simon. My confusion and shock must have been apparent. They laughed when Mutt explained they were nicknames, as they all had forgotten their real names. Everyone laughed with joy and friendship which was evident. Never had I been so humbled and grateful for being given the opportunity of a lifetime. Weasel was just over five feet tall. He had a thin face, pointed nose and narrow chin. He had small, but very white teeth that glistened when he smiled. His small frame was accentuated by very long arms. He seemed anxious and moved quickly and even talked faster than necessary. I was told by Dad that his appearance was the reason for his nickname.

Mutt, on the other hand, was short and stocky with a rugged, chubby face. He had very little hair and his baldness fit his body frame. He had fingers that were crooked and seemed swollen. I heard that his weird fingers were the result of being a catcher and hockey goalie. Leo was tall and graceful-looking, with wavy, white hair. He was always was well-tanned, which accented his blue eyes. I noticed he had bushy eyebrows that needed trimming, but they somehow fit his appearance. Long, rugged fingers and larger-than-normal wrists gave him a presence that was confident. He was the pitcher on the team. Simple Simon had a light complexion with grey eyes. His nose appeared broken and crooked. He was stocky and well built, with strong legs. Simon had scars around his eyes and his ears were much larger than normal. His completely bald head shined and appeared waxed. Simon had been a boxer, and he had the battle scars to prove it. He was very mild-mannered, which somehow seemed to contradict his boxing career. Every one of these men had survived by fighting and clawing their way through life.

Mutt asked me how long it would take for me to hang my first rack. Simple Simon said, "Probably not as long as it took you, Mutt." My father informed everyone that Uncle Lee was in charge of that adventure.

Weasel asked, "What's new?" Sitting down on my stool, it was obvious there was more living experience in this room than anywhere in the world. That's what I felt at the time and even more so now. On my uncle's desk sat a mount of a huge barn owl with large yellow glass eyes that looked in all directions. I asked where the owl came from.

Leo answered, "I hit him with my truck." Simple Simon replied that it was a good thing, because Leo sure as hell couldn't have shot him. Everyone snickered.

As the door opened, bells rang alerting us to the presence of a customer. The man rang the bell located near the cash register. Uncle Lee slowly got up and reached for a lunch bag, which he carried toward the customer. Everyone was still when we overheard Uncle Lee ask if this man needed a quarter. The air was surprisingly silent until the man left the store. Returning to his chair, my uncle explained the man was Walking Charlie. He was very slow and poor. He had always known him and tried to help Charlie when possible. Uncle Lee felt sorry for Walking Charlie. Whenever Charlie needed food or a few cents, he knew he could always depend on my uncle. Uncle Lee told me that Charlie was harmless and advised me to never abuse that reality.

My father offered some wisdom by saying that Charlie had grown up around Uncle Lee. They had been friends and neighbors for over sixty years. My uncle never said a word and neither did the other men. They also skirted any more discussion about Charlie. Weasel asked if there was any sign of the monster buck on Clayton's land. Uncle Lee said that he hadn't seen any tracks lately, but felt the old bastard was still deep in the swamp. Leo refrained with, "That old buck was going to outsmart everyone again this season." It was then that Uncle Lee informed his audience that he developed a theory that would guarantee success, and everyone laughed except Dad and me.

Reluctantly, I asked, "How big is that buck?"

Simple Simon looked around and replied, "He's at least two hundred and sixty pounds, with a rack of either twelve or fourteen points." Pointing to the huge rack on the wall, Mutt stated that the buck in question would dwarf that mount. Obviously my visualization was limited, but from the topic of the conversation, I realized that this buck had eluded everyone concerned. Everyone in this fraternity had seen him, and missed him. They all hoped to bag the old buck before he died of old age.

My Uncle chipped in with, "I've missed him twice and its not going to happen again." My father softly poked my arm with a subtle message to shut up. My uncle spit into his pail, standing up with energy, he declared, "That old bastard has humiliated me enough, and his rack will be on this wall next year at this time."

The old men all said "Lee, you've been saying that for the past four years, so it's time to put up or shut up."

My Uncle stared at Mutt and replied, "If it wasn't for the other three friends, he would have had to buy his meat from the butcher."

Dad stepped in and commented, "That old buck has caused more hard feelings than necessary."

Leo, who seemed calmer, quietly stated, "Whomever shoots this old buck will need three days to drag him out of the swamp." That lightened the conversation, but it was evident that even though these old men were attached at the hip, they were also fiercely competitive. Uncle Lee asked Leo if he was ready for trapping season and wondered if he had any beaver castor left from the previous year. Leo said yes, but he needed it. Uncle Lee snickered and asked if there wasn't enough to share, then the fox urine he had was also in short supply. Leo laughed and said, "Stop over, I might have a castor or two in the shed." My uncle replied that he knew that he had seen them hanging on the wall, drying. Leo shook his head in disbelief then replied, "You don't miss a trick." All the men laughed, stood up and slowly started to exit the store reluctantly. This reaction indicated that these rustic gentlemen were and had been friends their entire lives. My father said goodbye to these guys and they all rustled my hair as they walked by. I felt proud and accepted by the friends of my Uncle Lee and Dad.

Sitting alone with Dad and Uncle Lee, the conversation was direct and pointed, with some detail that renewed my interest in that old buck. The questions surrounding this massive whitetail were openly discussed and the intrigue was heavy with anticipation evident in my dad and uncle. It was surprisingly exhilarating to hear the honest and open dialogue between these two men that I was dependent on. It was evident that the coming deer season had one objective. The store was being prepared for closing, which didn't take long, and the three of us walked into the evening that was typical fall weather. Light rain was falling and the wind was blowing leaves in circles around the entryways of the stores. The air smelled like a garden that had been freshly tilled. My uncle offered good night and referred to the smell of autumn that defined the connection between the three of us.

CHAPTER 7

Serious Discussions with Dad

During the ride home I was asked if I had been surprised by my first encounter with my uncle's friends. Thinking about the multitude of feelings, I think my response surprised my father. I told him that I didn't feel comfortable referring to the man as Simple Simon. He started laughing hysterically, and after composing himself, he said to just call him "Simple" and started laughing again. "On second thought, maybe you should just call him nothing," he said. I laughed and said that was a great name. We both laughed all the way home and we were still laughing as we entered the house.

My mom went into hysterics when Dad explained the humor. "My God, Ray, you're really in for a treat with the five musketeers," she said. I laughed again and described poor Walking Charlie, and that's when both parents drew the line. They explained some details of Charlie's life, which changed my opinion immediately. As I was being tucked into bed, my father explained that regardless of the conversations that took place in the store to always remember that those men and a few I would yet meet had played baseball and hockey, hunted, fished and trapped, and were loyal and loving friends for over fifty years. It's also important to pay close attention and speak only when asked. You have the opportunity of a lifetime. It's extremely important to earn and keep their respect.

My dad continued his effort to educate me with a statement that has remained part of my value system. The message was, "Ray, those old men have seen, heard, discussed, argued, dissected and prayed openly for their entire lives, and unfortunately, only a handful of people will ever appreciate the knowledge and educations they have regarding life itself. How right he was. To be completely honest, old trophy whitetails had probably kept those old men going for years. That was my first night in the pipe aroma office, and I wanted it to last forever. As young as I was, it was the first time that I was completely filled with a feeling of gratitude.

The next day, meeting my friends and walking to school, the typical conversation regarding the Yankees and Dodgers dominated the arguments and there was one lone Cardinal fan. Baseball cards were being traded and each of us had a couple pennies to invest at Sam's store. Spelling wasn't the priority and as life would have it, the obsession to learn spelling was put on the back burner. One of my friends mentioned that the village was going to have a Little League Baseball organization the following spring, which didn't mean much at the time. None of us had ever heard of Little League, so the topic was changed to Mickey Mantle and Duke Snider. School was only a necessary evil in our day's activity. Finally, the school day was over and all my friends started for Sam's Store to hopefully purchase some new baseball cards before our rich friend Arsen bought them all. Arsen was always buying twenty-five cards at a time, which aggravated me and my other penny customers. After buying two cards and chewing the bubble gum, I said goodbye to my buddies and headed for the shortcut home. Skipping along the old dirt path, I was met by Freckles, who was usually waiting under the sumac trees, which were bright red and maroon this time of year. Patting my hound, we galloped freely toward home. I picked up a stick and threw it for Freckles to fetch, but he had grown tired of that game. Running onto the porch, I put my spelling book on the rail and turned and headed for the trapper's shed. The Nash was gone and I hoped the doors to his cave were left open. They were and I walked inside. Traps were hung drying and the odor of bait was apparent. I noticed a paper note in the vice and it was written to me. I will always remember the message: "Ray, if you're in here don't touch the traps that are hanging. Human scent on these traps renders them useless." Two pairs of black rubber gloves were sitting on a stool, and it was no surprise that one pair would fit my uncle and the other fit me. The Adirondack backpack was sitting on the workbench and some tools had been laid out neatly for my observation.

As I turned around, my dad was walking through the garage looking for me. I yelled, "I'm in here."

He acknowledged me by replying, "I know." As he walked into the shed, he explained that my enthusiasm was a concern and he wanted to make sure that I didn't handle any freshly dyed traps. Dad surprised me when he asked if I felt better calling Simple Simon by Simon only.

I said, "Yes, but the name nothing was funny." He agreed, but suggested to leave it at Simon. We had a conversation regarding the trapping tools and the explanations were easy enough to understand. Dad sat down in the tan recliner with ease, and I suddenly realized that he had spent a great deal of time in this shed, and it obviously felt like home to him. That's when I asked if he knew how to trap like Uncle Lee and he smiled with the answer yes. I asked, "Why then are you not helping?" His answer was ingrained into my memory.

"Ray, your uncle needs to feel needed and wants you to enjoy the same things he loves, and I think he knows that someday you're going to continue in his footsteps. This is a very large and loving expectation that he has, but I also feel you're the logical choice. Did you notice how easy and relaxed the old men were last night?"

I responded, "No."

"Well, those old friends have been told by Uncle Lee that they are also involved in your education and they accepted that choice last night," he said. I fumbled with confusion and asked how he knew. "I've been around those old codgers for years and trust me, they will willingly allow your presence when it's appropriate."

The four friends of my uncle had talents regarding trapping skills. Weasel specialized in mink, Mutt was better at beaver while Leo enjoyed rats and coons. Your uncle really knows fox trapping, so every one of those men have at least fifty years of experience to share with each other and now you. I was suddenly filled with some feelings of pressure; Dad sensed my temperament and reassured me that everyone of those grizzly old men were kind and understanding.

During the week before trapping season opened, life was complicated with realities that perpetuated some serious decisions I was forced to make. With responsibilities and multitasking becoming evident in my life, being confronted with life's expectations at my age was a bit unnerving. School, from my perspective, was taking more time than necessary. Life would have been much easier without added pressure being applied toward spelling, reading and math. Schoolwork complicated my comfort zone. The constant battle for maintaining acceptable grades caused me to feel threatened. In reality, my priorities were certainly not in the classroom. On top of schoolwork, I was expected to handle jobs around the house and deal with my hounds. On occasion, I was also expected to play and interrelate with my sister. Leaves needed attention and my baseball cards needed to be arranged by teams. Man, life was becoming complicated.

I was beginning to confront problems with negotiation skills and tried to manipulate those significant adults to no avail. My mom had no sense of humor regarding schoolwork and Dad demanded chores be done with consistency, coupled with proper execution. To make matters worse, there was a parent-teacher meeting coming up and the holiday pageant at school would interfere with my free time. Being chosen for a solo in the Christmas play generated additional pressure and for the first time I could remember, balance in my life seemed impossible. After all, my uncle and his cronies were preparing for my official introduction to trapping. I certainly couldn't renege on that priority. Sitting on the green porch swing with Freckles, I had a feeling of desperation at the ripe old age of eleven. What was once a perfect life seemed to be crashing down around me, and so I did what anyone would have done in my situation. I cried in frustration and decided to share these issues with Uncle Lee. This had not been a typical carefree day free of performance issues and things were going to get worse before supper. My dad was driving into the driveway. My lack of composure was noticed and he asked, "What's wrong?"

I replied, "Nothing."

He came back with, "Then why are your cheeks dirty and eyes red?" The jig was up and the fountain of youth spilled out with tears and frustration flowing as I blurted my guts out. Even my frustration regarding my friend Arsen buying all the baseball cards was aired. Standing in front of me and Freckles, my dad looked concerned and slowly reached out to comfort me. My father had never been confronted before by my emotional well-being so magnified. He usually had to comfort me when tears flowed if I was physically hurt. I knew my behavior was non-typical and probably would result in having to go to the reform school. My mom, who had been preparing supper, joined Dad and me on the porch. When she realized my dilemma, she seemed a bit frantic. It was the first time, my father firmly told mom that he would handle this matter and she reluctantly backed off. My dad somehow understood, and with a caring smile, sat down and put his arm around me for comfort and it worked. The first thing he asked was, "Why does Arsen buying all the baseball cards bother you so much?"

My answer was, "Sam never has any pennies and it's not fair."

Dad explained that Arsen's parents had money and that was his only enjoyment. He was right, and I also knew that my friend lived a very controlled life. "As far as Sam is concerned, you have extra cards and several duplicates; think about giving some to him." I thought about it and decided it was a great idea.

The next issue was the leaf problem, which was solved easily when Dad referred to the constant drizzle that made it difficult to rake. That solved that problem. "Now for the studies, you're doing well, except for your spelling issue, and I haven't gotten involved until now," he said. "The teacher and your mom expect you to sound out the words using vowels and syllables," which made sense, but my method of learning spelling was to memorize the words on the test. "Try that approach. That might be the answer to that issue.

The parent-teacher conference is just an excuse for your mom and Mrs. Smith to talk regarding your potential. It really won't surprise me that she will say, 'He could do better if he would apply himself.'" So what's new? What a relief to have some support.

"During the past few weeks, your life has been a bit emotional, and it's normal to feel responsible for results that can't be determined. In the total picture, you're doing extremely well, and regardless, I've been very proud of your behavior. Your relationship with Uncle Lee is really important and I will protect you if I feel you're being pressured excessively in areas that don't really matter. Please don't ever carry those types of feelings alone. Always come to me and we'll attempt to work through the problem together," said my caring parent.

My father was always more perceptive regarding feelings exhibited by my sister and myself. It was probably a result of being faced with having to live with seven brothers and three sisters. I recall thinking how complicated and confusing his school days must have been. During supper, my sister was gibbering about the doll on the cover of the Christmas catalogue and I sensed that she was anticipating Santa before Thanksgiving. Her life seemed simple enough and uncomplicated because she was a great student. All girls seemed smarter in school than boys, with the exception of one girl in my class who really struggled and cried a lot. Most of my classmates felt sympathy for her, but my teacher wasn't always understanding. Even at my age, I was developing a plan that would help this poor girl avoid humiliation.

After supper, it appeared a trip to the liquor store might not transpire. The drama performed on the porch was extremely evident, since my parents seemed a bit cool. While my dad listened to the local news and checked the box scores, the decision about the liquor store was probably going to be avoided. I felt responsible for putting my dad in a very difficult position. I knew if he had his druthers he wanted to spend an hour with the cronies. Putting down the paper, he asked if I knew that Mickey Mantle had hit two homers against

Washington and I replied yes, adding that Yogi Berra had also hit one.

The conversation about baseball and the Yankees was a bit different because my father was a Dodger fan. Standing with his paper folded and placed on the coffee table, he startled me by saying, "Get your coat and hat if your work is finished." I really loved my dad at that moment.

CHAPTER 8

Lessons Regarding Life and Nature

The rain had subsided, but the temperature had dropped considerably and the car's heater was turned on and running. I remembered that cooler temperatures were necessary for guard hair growth. I mentioned that reaction to dad and he offered more information. The temperature was only part of the equation; the change in daylight hours was also important. Obviously, I was trying to comprehend that information. He suggested that I throw that topic to the cronies and find out how they felt about it. The smell of pipe tobacco was pleasant, but my father held the door open to clear the interior of the store. I walked casually toward the office area as though I had been coming here my entire life. Weasel greeted me with, "Hello sport," and I simply acknowledged everyone. There was room on the old brown couch and Simple Simon patted the cushion, indicating for me to sit down. Every one of these old men wore green dickey work pants with red, brown or green suspenders. They also had hunting caps the same color. Their shirts were different colors and they were all neatly pressed.

Mutt said, "We were just talking about naming that trophy buck. Your uncle suggested that we should let you have a say." It was exhilarating to be included in this process. Dad had closed the door and meandered down into the office. He preferred to stand. My father was wearing jeans like myself and I thought some habits must be hard to break. My uncle wanted me to offer a name, which I did. The name I suggested was Fat Earl and everyone agreed that was very appropriate. My Uncle Lee referred to Fat Earl's track and it was the first time I heard the word dewclaw. Apparently, this huge buck had lost a dewclaw on his right rear foot.

My father intervened with, "Ray doesn't know about deer tracks."

It was then I interrupted my father by saying I knew what deer tracks look like. Mutt asked where I had learned that and I answered that I often jumped deer down the Dusty Trail. After a rain, animals left tracks around the puddles and the edge of the frog pond. My uncle laughed and suggested that Mutt would appreciate a lesson regarding tracks. Leo remained subdued and appeared a bit disengaged. I wondered if he was always quiet. I made an attempt to include him by asking where he lived and was surprised to learn his home was two streets from my house. I walked by his home often and he told me that I was welcome to stop any time I was in the neighborhood.

The decisions regarding packing the trapping supplies Friday night took immediate priority and my father offered to help prepare proper packing and arranging of the traps. He surprised my friends when he offered to help them, too. Simple Simon thanked him and asked if my dad could carry some weights to his truck that he needed for beaver drowning sets. My uncle injected that Simon was going to join us Saturday morning to assist in making our sets, and then we were going to help him. I realized that these rustic partners had reached the age when they helped each other perform tasks that they had done on their own for years. The inevitable aging process was clear and difficult for these old trappers to admit. I was informed by Uncle Lee that I needed the hip waders he had ordered at Levine's Store. They had arrived, and Dad should pick them up before Friday. My father asked how much they cost and was told they were an early Christmas gift. Dad replied, "Thank you."

While the topic of trapping was bantered around, Mutt reached into his pants pocket and handed me a wrapped butterscotch candy. Leo noticed and made reference to the fact that Mutt never shared his candy with the musketeers. Mutt smiled and rebutted, "Ray earned this candy by putting up with Leo."

Humor was always evident between these codgers, and it was usually at the expense of another friend. Simple Simon also piped in that butterscotch wasn't his favorite flavor and he preferred peppermint. Mutt turned and offered, "He obviously knew, which is why he had butterscotch." My uncle laughed and openly admitted that raccoons love peppermint. Thinking back over that conversation, the obsession these men had with the outdoors was always on their minds. It would never be possible to avoid that characteristic.

Recalling details that surfaced during these events perpetuates emotions which have continued to haunt me for over sixty years. Even though I have attempted to understand the significance of these rituals, the lasting impression these events left with me helped mold my basic personality. It also truly allows me to recall the time spent together as vividly as if it was yesterday.

As everyone was walking out of the store, there was little conversation; however, the feelings that encompassed these personalities was spiritual in nature. I realized even then that moments and friends like these were priceless. The respect and love was obvious and never can I remember these old codgers feeling intimidated by showing those feelings.

While my father was visiting with Leo, plans were being firmed up for a formal meeting Thursday evening in the office. I was expected to attend and my father was given that instruction by Weasel. My dad accepted those instructions with a grin and I felt he was gracious and pleased by that invitation.

Locking the door, Uncle Lee turned toward his friends and asked if they wanted to join him for a cold beer at the Silver Grill. They all accepted and seemed a bit excited to have a break in this routine that been a custom for more years than could be accounted for.

On the way home, the subject of friends surfaced from dad. It was the appropriate time for him to explain some details that I should try to digest. He went into detail about not having a dad or grandfather. With honesty, he explained that for me to have one dad and five grandfathers was emotional for him to observe. He delicately explained that these old men had suddenly gotten more enthusiastic about trapping and he knew it was because they wanted to enjoy my first experience doing the same thing they had done for over fifty years.

Dad went on with an explanation he felt I would understand. "Ray," he directed, "you will be shown and encouraged by legends in the trapping community. I don't want you to feel intimidated and reluctant. Just absorb as much as you're capable of. Trust me when I say someday down the road, these old men will be reborn."

That was heavy duty, and I simply replied, "I understand and feel accepted. That's all that matters at this time."

I explained that I wish he would get more involved, and his answer surprised me. He said he would make every attempt to join us because the enthusiasm had fired him up, also. He was aware of the fact that being involved with his uncle and four old friends who had committed to helping his son learn trapping skills had gone beyond the mechanics, and he wanted to share these emotional times firsthand.

He said, "You're very young to realize the complicated feelings being displayed, yet I sense you're more aware than even I know." I shrugged my shoulders and honestly tried to explain to my dad that I understood the desire to learn and teach from my relationship with him and Uncle Lee.

As we pulled into the drive, my father gave me some information he felt I needed. "Ray, no one in your class will ever have this opportunity to learn lessons regarding life and nature, and I've made that case to your mom and she understands. I suggest you make an attempt to tolerate school and your studies." I looked at the leaves on the ground, looked toward the trappers shed, then I told my father that Uncle Lee had given me the same advice and I knew I was expected to make an honest attempt.

Life returned to normal for a couple of days. Trips to the store were eliminated for two nights, which allowed me time to get my baseball cards organized. I carefully put some aside for Sam. I tried memorizing spelling words and it appeared to work better. I was also able to rake some leaves and placed several piles over the garden.

Thursday morning, I tried on my waders and they fit. School was fairly uneventful with the exception of talk about the World Series between the Yankees and Dodgers scheduled to start in a week. In those days, the World Series took over the entire town. One of my best friends, Joey, was such an avid Dodger fan he could quote statistics regarding Dodger players when they played in the minors. He even knew details about their families. I never forgot his ability to win arguments involving disputes about players and teams. He was a textbook of facts that he often backed up if challenged. The only way to win with Joey was for the Yanks to beat the Dodgers. My dad was always on Joey's side, which made matters worst.

Reliving those days brings back fond memories that put today's baseball tradition to shame. Baseball represented everything good during those years. I remember the starting lineups for every team myself, which is a bit of trivia I'm still proud of. I certainly cannot recall the players' parents like Joe; however, I remain nostalgic about those days and my young peers at that time.

CHAPTER 9

Preparing for the Big Event

Finally, Thursday evening rolled around and Dad seemed excited about accepting his role on the trap lines. I refer to lines because the old codgers had purposely gotten involved with each other's trap lines for companionship and help. Mom displayed some enthusiasm herself when she reminded me to listen closely because she knew that this opportunity was the beginning of my transition from being a spectator to a starting assignment on the musketeer's team. I was happy with her reaction. My sister was doing her typical girl things. She was involved with girlfriends on the street. She was also a bit excited about trapping, since she was surrounded by males who were obsessed with this lifestyle.

During supper, my father informed me that he had taken Friday off work and I would be allowed to leave school early at noon. I was flabbergasted and immediately realized my luck was changing. I asked why he had decided to take the day off and his answer was indicative of his commitment to the old codgers. He realized they all needed some help getting started, which would obviously take time. It was then he referred to each of these men and their ages, which changed the parameters surrounding their enthusiasm. My mother chirped that Dad was as bad as Uncle Lee getting all excited over this coming trapping season. Then my dad explained that it had been years since he had felt a fire in his belly to get involved with the trapping experience.

The time had arrived for the trappers meeting in the office area. While my dad and I were making a decision about coats needed for fall weather, there was a comfortable feeling of companionship evident between us. It's difficult to explain these observations, because either my dad had regressed to my age or I had slowly started to mature. Both observations are probably accurate. Before entering the car, we headed toward the trapper's shed for an inventory of Uncle Lee's preparation. My father seemed curious about his diligence in preparing for opening day. Dad seemed pleased with the evidence in the shed and replied, "Everything is in order, like it always is."

Getting into the car, my curiosity managed to surface and I asked what he was looking for. His answer was short and pointed. "Just making sure Uncle Lee still can manage." I found this unnerving, since my uncle was always prepared. While we walked toward the car, Freckles barked for attention. I felt some guilt, which was the product of serious emotional neglect. The past few days were filled with responsibilities that left very little time to engage my pet with affection.

The ride toward the meeting was filled with anticipation on my part, however. Dad was relaxed and seemed calm. It was obvious that his three days off were being enjoyed. Pulling into the parking space, I noticed a vehicle that looked like Martha's. Dad also recognized the car. I asked a question that obviously created some raw emotion within my father. I wanted to know and understand the complete story behind Uncle Lee and Martha. Dad simply nodded okay and offered to explain the entire circumstances surrounding the relationship at another time. He suddenly seemed preoccupied, and I was somewhat confused. Thinking back, it must have been difficult for my dad to explain a love affair to his eleven-year-old son.

Making our way along the sidewalk, the sun was setting and the fall sunset gave off soft yellow and orange lighting that typified fall sunsets in the area. My father also noticed the lighting and remarked how beautiful the evening was. With a pat on the butt, my father reminded me to allow these codgers to determine the plans regarding opening day.

Making our way into the store, the bells rang, signifying our arrival. It was apparent that a dutiful woman changed the behavior of the old codgers and for that matter, even my dad. The conversation was polite and filled with generalizations. Martha said hello, approached me and handed me a photo of Freckles with an engraved tribute for his victory. It was a great picture and I have often wondered where that ever ended up. It hung in the office over the desk for many years.

Martha softly told my uncle she would call later and excused herself by replying that she needed to shop for groceries. She patted my shoulder and reminded me that these old men needed my help, and they all laughed. My uncle stood and walked her to the door. She said, "Enjoy your trapping season and stay in touch."

After Martha left, plans were being made for Dad to drive over to each of the four codgers to assist them in anyway they needed. It was determined that Uncle Lee and I would prepare his Nash after he picked me up at school at noon. The one thing that was obvious created some serious discussion between the musketeers. They were all anxious to be present around my intro to a trap line. They all agreed to meet at Clayton's farm Saturday morning at six. That seemed early, but I stayed silent. Mutt offered that the beaver needed four sets and Leo could target rats and coons. Weasel could help me with some mink sets along the creek and Mutt could eat his butterscotch candies while he watched. Simple Simon was instructed to help explain the process to me when necessary, because he was obviously the most skilled of all.

Dad offered some advice that applied to everyone present. He insisted on doing the heavy work and if necessary, would wade the deeper water. Everyone seemed to be in agreement. These old gentlemen insisted that they spend most of the day together helping get all types of sets out on what they called Ray's line. I later realized what a sacrifice they made disregarding their own lines for the weekend. My father made a very profound statement by thanking each of them for taking a sincere interest in his son and said he couldn't thank them enough. Leo replied, "Leon, you realize that my grandson would have been Ray's age, and we all want to participate in teaching and experiencing the fun and enjoyment we anticipate."

Simple Simon was assigned to fox sets and explained that his feeling was there were at a minimum of four sets necessary for proper coverage. It was then I was introduced to the fact that fox trapping was completely different than water trapping, which would be discussed in detail after all the water traps were set. I was confused about my uncle not being mentioned in regard to making sets. I slowly worked up enough nerve to ask the codgers why my uncle was not going to be involved. My uncle came forth with a simple explanation that he was going to be the supervisor of everyone. It was unique for these musketeers to admit that Uncle Lee had forgotten more about trapping than they knew. Weasel told me that my uncle could swim like a mink and think like a fox. I smiled with acceptance.

With the meeting winding down, the mood started to change, and for some reason these men were reluctant to leave the store. My dad picked up on these feelings and told me it was time to leave. As I slowly started to put on my coat, there was a sincere gesture made by my uncle when he stood, hitched his green dickeys, reached down under his desk and pulled out a Spalding baseball mitt and handed it to me. Realizing my chin was quivering with emotion, he told me a shortstop needed a good leather glove.

Trying on the glove, the smell of new leather was powerful. I was speechless, and Dad injected it was an autographed mitt by Phil Rizzuto. My Friends said it should be signed by Pee Wee Reese. Then they all laughed when I predicted the Yanks would win in six games.

As we all made our way out of the store, these old men all took my glove and spit in the pocket and rubbed it into the leather. Then they referred to my uncle's quickness on the ball field. Mutt replied that Lee could field, but lacked a predictable stick. My uncle replied that Mutt was the only catcher that never threw anyone out at second. They all razzed each other for a few minutes and then we all left for home.

During the ride, emotion was heavy in the car, and my dad asked if I wanted to join him for a soda. Hess Drugstore was still open and we had time. A soda sounded good. Sitting in a small booth next to my father, I was filled with gratitude and was grateful for having a dad, uncle and friends who showed their feelings openly.

My father mentioned that Uncle Lee wanted to buy that mitt and had asked him if it was alright. He then explained that regardless of the results, the old codgers had adopted me as their own. Little did I realize at the time how lucky I was, and I didn't anticipate the responsibility that these feelings would eventually create.

My dad really understood the significance of this evening and sat silently, enjoying his soda. After all this time, memories of that evening always lift my heart. The internal comfort these experiences created have remained with me every opening of trapper's season and the start of the World Series.

On the drive home, plans were made for an early breakfast, and we needed to have everything ready and organized to eliminate confusion Friday evening and more importantly, Saturday morning.

Up and having breakfast with my family, I was told that dad would drop my sister and me off at school. He planned on starting at Mutt's home and work through the rest of the codgers. Nothing out of the ordinary was expected, and he felt he would be finished shortly after noon. He hoped to be available for Uncle Lee and myself by at least one p.m.

When I left school at noon, my excitement peaked and I ran all the way home. The weather was nice, with a slight chance of a shower. I dropped off my books and headed for the shed, where my uncle sat napping in the tan recliner. To my surprise, the first thing out of uncle's mouth was, "Go get your waders, we need to wash and prepare them for trapping." The black rubber gloves were sitting on the stool, and they also needed preparation. Obviously, I had no idea what these instructions had to do with trapping, but I was going to find out. As I walked behind the Nash, the trunk was open and it was filled with pine and cedar branches that had been freshly cut. I always loved the smell of fresh cedar and pine.

Washing our waders with soap and water to eliminate human odor, we turned them upside-down and hung each boot from the ropes of the deer hanging rack. Each pair of rubber gloves was cleaned thoroughly and they were also hung.

During this cleaning process, a detailed explanation of no contamination was defined in detail and emphasized somewhat radically. Just about everything being discussed was about contamination, which remains the secret of successful fox and coyote trapping today.

My dad pulled into the drive and approached us with comfort and confidence. My uncle told Dad that most everything was properly prepared and all we needed to do was let the boots and gloves dry. He also referred to the fox traps behind the garage with the backpack and fox trapping supplies. I never noticed traps or equipment missing from the shed. I mentioned that to Dad and Uncle Lee and they smiled knowingly. "Sometimes your curiosity gets you in trouble, so we hid them on you to eliminate that possibility," they said. I was humiliated, but over some time, I knew they were right.

My uncle asked about the cronies and a conversation about their preparation indicated that every one was up to snuff. Uncle Lee slipped and made mention of Mutt's poor health and checked himself quickly. Nothing more was said at that time.

My uncle reached for my gloves, but before he touched them with bare hands he used leaves to handle them to avoid human contamination. I was shocked by these extremes and said so. It was the first time my uncle snarled at me and told me point-blank that I was to follow his instructions, because the development of poor fundamentals will lead to failure. I know now just how right he was. It still hurt my feelings and my dad didn't even come to my defense. Just like I said, "Right is right, so do it right the first time."

The decisions regarding numbers and sizes of traps were written down for my dad to plan distribution in the trunk. Taking the list, he started toward the shed and then returned to get uncle's rubber gloves. He turned toward me and replied, "See how easy it is to forget about contamination?" I nodded yes. After placing traps on the cedar and pine branches, he covered them with extra branches. He told me that all the water traps would be on the left. After he was satisfied, he slowly walked toward the back of the shed to fetch the fox traps and equipment. The pains being taken was a bit difficult to digest, but I shut my mouth. The last thing he did was get the backpack, and in his other hand he had a green pail with a cover that held the bait, lure and fox urine. This whole process was intense for me to observe, but both Dad and Uncle Lee performed this ritual with precision. A list was pulled out of uncle's pocket and he slowly started checking off details. Once finished, he slowly closed the trunk.

"Well Ray, now you can ask all your questions," he said, and they both smiled deliberately. I told them I pretty much understood and they both laughed. With some effort, I participated in the joke. Then my dad reached inside his jacket and pulled out a trapper's how-to book and handed it to me. Uncle Lee asked where he got it and he replied it was from Leo. My uncle seemed happy and sad at the same time. He opened the book and inside was a note written to someone named Leo, Jr. from Grandpa. It was the moment of truth regarding Leo's subdued moods that occasionally surfaced. His grandson had drowned at the age of ten when he had wandered out of the yard and they found him in a small frog pond pretty close to the dusty trail. Even at my age, this reality created empathy and compassion for my new friend Leo. Of all the codgers, Leo displayed the lowest profile, yet I knew he was a force to be reckoned with. I made a decision to attempt to understand his loss and internal pain. My feelings were prevalent and Uncle Lee replied, "Leo needs to feel wanted and needed." He also informed me that Leo had offered his help educating me and that was the beginning of all the musketeers' interest in this pursuit. Dad reminded me that I shouldn't bring these facts up to Leo unless he offers a need to mention that situation. As luck would have it, that reality would raise its head in two days.

CHAPTER 10

A True Sense of Belonging (or Smell)

With all the details finished, my father suggested that we all go into the shed and relax with a beer and root beer for me. Uncle Lee seemed relaxed and filled with emotions that I had only seen in my uncle when he was involved with nature and wildlife pursuits. Sitting around the shed with my seventy-year-old uncle and my father, who was thirty-two, my sense of belonging was elevated when dad referred to the three old trappers sitting around a potbelly stove reminiscing over the past. Uncle Lee smiled and said, "You know Leon, that this family has produced some of the best outdoorsmen, and the tradition will hopefully continue forever." I never forgot that statement and even at my age today I know he was correct in his observation.

The subject of the trophy buck was discussed and three significant facts came to the forefront. That old buck knew that swamp and rarely left his sanctuary. It was apparent that he also knew everyone of the musketeers, since they had all attempted to hang that rack. Every one of these old gentleman had horror stories about this old buck's ability to outsmart them all.

The only fear was that this old buck was going to win in the end. My father and uncle talked about this deer as though they knew him personally. I was captivated by the intensity and tenacity that flowed throughout the conversation. My uncle said that this buck grew moss on his rack during the summer and was ghostlike in his movements. I was riveted by this story and with my limited visualization skills, wanted the opportunity to at least see Fat Earl. My uncle and father had seen Fat Earl twenty feet behind Mutt crawling on his belly, but neither my uncle nor father could shoot for safety reasons. My father said that this buck was grey when he was a crotch horn. It was then that I suggested we change the name from Fat Earl to the Grey Ghost. My uncle agreed and the name Grey Ghost would circulate and become a legend in the community. It was already a topic of conversation among the whitetail hunters in the area.

It was then that I stood both Dad and uncle on their ears when I explained that I could smell deer and could tell the difference between bucks and does. They both stood and reacted as if they had seen a real ghost. In unison, they asked if I knew what I was talking about. Obviously, I was defensive with their disbelief. I went on to explain that the deer around the dusty trail often times would hang around the pond and I knew them by smell. It was the first time I heard Uncle Lee take the Lord's name in vain when he said, "Jesus Christ, Leon, that kid of yours has a nose like Freckles." Then they both laughed and wanted more information. I went on to tell of several occasions when I smelled deer before I saw them. I also divulged that I thought everyone could smell deer. Uncle Lee sat down perplexed and shook his head with bewilderment and then he replied "God Damn, Ray your nose is worth a million dollars and whatever you do, keep this between your father and me. Then he said, "I knew I picked a winner." I deferred to showing them and wanted to make believers out of them. They understood, which pleased me and I was aware of the potential of my nose. It's laughable today, but for a kid of eleven , it was a powerful weapon for the future deer hunts. As we left the shed to clean up before supper and bed, both adults were excited about my ability to smell deer and make the distinction between bucks and does. I realized that I had gained some significant power and felt somewhat special.

Uncle Lee got into his Nash and headed for the store, which he would close at nine. Walking toward our porch with my dad, there seemed to be contentment present and when my sister met us. Dad picked her up and gave her a kiss. My sister and dad were very close, and they remained that way his entire life. That was as wholesome and honest a relationship I ever observed between a father and daughter. She and I often reminisce about our youth with love and understanding.

Supper was great and the anticipation for Saturday morning hung in the air. My mom asked if all went well and dad offered, "Better than expected."

She said "I hope tomorrow is as good, and Sunday will determine the success of everyone's effort."

My sister turned her head towards the back door and replied, "There's a deer in the garden." My father asked where and she replied she couldn't see it, but she could smell it. Both parents looked at each other and I just shrugged my shoulders.

CHAPTER 11

Transfer of Knowledge and Love of Nature

The morning came quickly, and even with my excitement I had difficulty coming alive. Eating breakfast with Dad was pleasant because he fried eggs better than Mom. The front door opened and Uncle Lee appeared for his share of breakfast. As we sat eating, my father told the story about my sister and uncle just shook his head in disbelief. The plan was to pick up Simple Simon and meet the other three at Clayton's around six. The weather was cool at around thirty-five degrees, which determined our clothing. Red jackets and hats were a necessity. Putting the dishes in the sink, we exited the house and walked to the Nash.

After picking up Simon, we headed toward Clayton's. Simon referred to the autumn colors and offered cited his love for this time of year. Simon also asked if the beaver sets were first. My uncle said yes and my dad asked Simon, "Do you realize the number of beaver in this area?"

Simon said, "Yes, I was there a few days ago."

My uncle replied, "You're looking for the Grey Ghost, you can't fool me." That was when we explained the name change from Fat Earl to Grey Ghost. Simon agreed with the name change. He offered that there was no sign of him and wondered if a poacher had shot him. Dad replied that we would have heard. Nobody would keep that to themselves. There was some concern regarding Mutt's health and my father told Simon that Mutt had been very energetic when he had helped him the day before.

Simon said, "That's great, because I worry about him." I was still a bit uncomfortable about all the concern with Mutt, but didn't ask any questions.

With some difficulty, I inquired about the procedure I was to follow and Simon told me to stick close to him or anyone else observing the sets being made. Uncle Lee openly referred to each old codger being extremely proficient in making all types of sets. The secret to trapping water animals was numbers and proper location of the appropriate set for that situation. That was obviously Greek to me, yet it wouldn't take long to learn the procedure. Daylight was breaking and there was a frost on the meadows, giving the illusion of a fresh snowfall. It was lovely. My excitement must have shown, because that's when Simon explained my only responsibility was to help when asked and to try and take in everything possible for future reference.

The sun was just breaking daylight, giving the fall foliage its moment in the sun. The one thing that stood out during my first opening day was the beauty that our quest allowed us to witness.

As the four of us rode with the other cronies, the unknown for myself started to elevate and pique my interest. A vehicle was spotted near our meeting at the small sand pit and our friends were leaning up against the truck sipping coffee. Every one of these old codgers was dressed with waders ready for beaver sets. The mood was elevated, due to the companionship. Pulling up and parking, we got out to join our friends. Uncle Lee walked toward the trunk and unlocked it to allow the beaver trappers to gain access to the traps and equipment needed.

Each of the cronies was wandering around the pond discussing the appropriate number of sets and type of set needed. They all gave me information that I filed away for future reference. Even though I knew nothing about beaver trapping, these old men made my introduction easy and comfortable. I won't bore you with details except that I was amazed at the knowledge and understanding of beaver behavior characteristics that was understood by every codger participating. I also noticed that there were no negative comments and every set location and technical details were easily agreed upon. The entire experience surrounding this endeavor was explained in a manner which an eleven-year-old could comprehend. The observations I made regarding these trappers as they performed the task of proper technical details was not only intriguing, but it was apparent that each old codger had over fifty years evolving as part of the environment rather than an intruder. I was given every opportunity to help and as the sets were being made, patience and explanations were graciously offered in a calm and gentle manner. Everyone was diligent in the details and there was so much respect evident. From my perspective at the time, it was magical and a bit mysterious.

My father helped as expected, and the relaxed mood was also evident within his personality. The emotional gratitude was all-encompassing, with each and every aspect of setting these traps, which had become a part of the lifestyle each of these old men, engrained in their existence. The rugged male image they swaggered with was filled with masculinity and circled with respect for nature and life itself. Thinking back to that experience, I was filled with anticipation and awe as I observed these codgers perform tasks that had become second nature to them, and in some respects it was old, yet infantile.

The mood was filled with comfort and somehow lacked the intensity that I had anticipated. My dad moved gracefully interacting with his friends and it appeared as though he totally understood his place in the pecking order. My uncle had a permanent smile stamped on his face which seemed serene and satisfied.

The entire process was emotional for everyone concerned, since the primary objective was to educate me on the basic fundamentals required for success. It was becoming obvious that each and every one realized the significance of their participation. I will never forget the humility and integrity that was displayed by these mystical old men. I gradually realized the significance of this education when the emotional feelings of friendship and security enveloped the entire experience. The internal feelings being expressed with serenity and awareness was flowing smoothly like the two small streams that fed this pond. The redwing blackbirds squawked and the pond was at peace within the universal placid illusion it offered. These rustic old gentlemen were being rejuvenated to a much younger time in their lives that they all embraced with gratitude and understanding.

It was slowly becoming evident that each and every movement was transfixed, as if it had been choreographed by a conductor. It wasn't just about successful catches. It seemed as though each and every one was totally at peace with where these challenges took these fine men. They all loved the outdoors and it was emotional to witness. It surfaced slowly within my limited experience that I wanted what they had, and I decided right then and there that my life would never be the same. The tranquil attitude displayed was injected into my being. The tranquility and peace that surrounded this pursuit was the beginning of my understanding about life and its emotional possibilities that were being gifted to me. Little did I realize the significance of this transformation of my personality, and I'm sure the impact of this introduction wasn't possible for anyone to predict.

The beaver sets were finished and the mink and muskrat sets were next. Leo and Weasel were suddenly elevated and they showed me in detail the proper trap placement while also injecting the animal's behavior characteristics. Digesting the information was difficult, yet it certainly seemed easier to retain than spelling. Each aspect made sense and it appeared to perpetuate logic and creativity.

CHAPTER 12

Grey Ghost Sighting

Leo and Weasel picked up their gear and the three of us slowly walked toward the two narrow streams which were to be targeted for mink and a few muskrats. Leo was sullen and Weasel was more enthusiastic, and I knew that Leo was torn about his grandson's death. I attempted to draw him out to no avail. He was a proud, stately man with a graceful nobility. I recall thinking that of all the old codgers, he was the most coordinated and athletic. I listened to Weasel explain about mink and understood the approach and basic techniques needed for trapping them. To be honest, I wasn't really very interested in mink or rats, but I realized the value of learning all I could. Leo was standing with his hands on his hips and he offered to help me set a number one trap I was having difficulty with. It was during this interaction that he called me "Junior." I could tell it was extremely difficult for him as he realized his mistake. Not knowing how to react, I tried to ignore this comparison, but it was dramatic for Leo. Tears formed in his eyes and ran down his cheeks. I felt he struggled with the pain internally. I fumbled around nervously, yet in the typical fashion I expected from Leo, he recovered and proceeded with his instruction.

It was then I thanked him for the trapper's manual and he made a very profound statement. He told me he had bought that manual for his grandson and wanted to give it to him for

Christmas. He continued saying that after Leo Junior passed, he felt empty and lacked motivation. He went on to say that getting involved with my interest in trapping could potentially help him heal and recover. I stammered awkwardly that I was sorry and in my stupidity asked what position he played on the ball team. He shuddered and responded pitcher. He continued by saying he had played in the minor leagues and had ruined his pitching arm. Not knowing where else to go in conversation, he slowly rearranged my trap placement and explained the reason. I was comfortable with Leo and he sensed that about me. After putting out lure, Leo rustled my hair with affection. Without saying anything, we both understood our friendship. In a critical time in Leo's life he needed to interact with a young person for selfish, emotional needs. As Leo and I made our way downstream, he appeared calm and was slowly recovering his composure. Weasel was setting some mink sets along the other stream and he appeared captivated by his task. Leo told me that Weasel was nervous and jerky by nature and to ignore his hyperactivity. I smiled and nodded in understanding.

While making a rat set with Leo, a slight breeze picked up and a familiar smell caught my attention. I looked up toward the bend in the creek. I nudged Leo and told him not to move a whisker. I slowly raised my head and there he was, the Grey Ghost. Looking at us with curiosity the Grey Ghost was standing along the shore and I was amazed by his size. He looked as big as a horse and had antlers like those of an elk that I had seen in National Geographic. Leo was fascinated. His eyes were sparkling with awe and disbelief. The Grey Ghost was on alert and seemed completely under control. . This huge whitetail was obviously the king of this swamp and the surrounding area. With grace and security, that huge buck bounded back into the swamp and disappeared in a flash.

Both Leo and I were mesmerized by this experience and then we both laughed nervously. Weasel, who had located himself upstream and around the bend, wasn't aware of the event that had taken over this trapping education. Leo remained calm and with some degree of disbelief, explained our encounter with the Grey Ghost to Weasel. The two friends exchanged tidbits about other sightings and they were both exhilarated with evidence that the Grey Ghost was still dominating the swamp. The breeze continued to pick up energy, which allowed a welcomed respite from the warm sun. With my limited knowledge and expertise, I offered an observation. That old buck knows everyone that enters his sanctuary and knew these old codgers were in the area, so his curiosity had gotten the better of him. I was asked by Leo what had alerted me to the presence of the Grey Ghost and I was forced to avoid mentioning the talent I had promised to keep just between Dad and Uncle Lee. I just said he caught my attention. Weasel, in his nervous, hyper manner, seemed perplexed with this deer appearing at midday and making himself vulnerable. Leo muttered that the Grey Ghost knew the hunting season wasn't open, but was also surprised with the midday sighting.

With all the water sets made, the three of us wandered upstream to join the rest of the cronies, and I was looking forward to lunch. The experience of the sighting was mulled over within this entourage and excitement was elevated to a fever pitch. My uncle wanted details from Leo, but never asked me what had transpired. I instinctively knew the reason he excluded my reaction. I was transfixed by stories and details of efforts that had been attempted in bagging the Grey Ghost with a multitude of theories that had obviously failed.

The difficulty these experienced old codgers had regarding failure to bag this buck surprised me. I apparently insulted everyone by expressing that opinion. Simple Simon spoke for each of them by curtly stating, "Your inexperience is show-ing, and please refrain from questioning our ability."

Dad came to my defense, saying, "Ray has never taken part in a deer hunt, but will understand better in the future." I must confess that my feelings were hurt, but I knew more than anyone realized regarding deer habits. I had watched sever-al deer around the Dusty Trail and felt comfortable with my observations. I had gained some personal feelings regarding deer habits.

With preparation being made for fox sets, my enthusiasm peaked to a level that wasn't present during the water sets. I walked with Simon toward a location he had picked for his set. The extremes being taken to eliminate contamination and obvious human scent and activity intrigued me. While Simon slowly made the set, my uncle explained the entire process in detail with an explanation of the subtle aspects of set prepa-ration. He slowly drew my attention to specific factors that only extremely successful trappers knew could be the differ-ence between success and failure. After Simon finished his set, Mutt walked slowly toward his location on the other side of the cornfield. With Uncle Lee, we walked carefully behind Mutt, and I was told not to spit or leave any scent. The radical extremes being utilized were strange and somewhat confus-ing. I knew how important these details were regarding fox trapping from previous conversations I'd had with Dad and Uncle Lee. While Mutt slowly made his version of a fox set, more details were pointed out. His set appeared somewhat different than Simon's, but both men seemed comfortable and confident in their presentation. The third location was select-ed by Leo, and he made a similar type set while Uncle Lee explained the differences each of the codgers made on their own. Leo's set appeared to be smaller in size than the other sets. During this practice session, I realized that fox trapping was an art and required more attention to detail than I ever anticipated.

My uncle decided to send the old codgers on their way by telling them we had decided to call it a day. Fortunately, they all agreed and admitted they were tired. After thanking each of them, they all mentioned meeting at the store around six p.m. I knew something was being kept close to the vest when Dad seemed a bit unnerved. After the codgers headed toward home, both Dad and uncle started an interrogation about my spotting the Grey Ghost. As we drove around the tote roads, Uncle Lee informed me that we were going to make a fox set in the sand pit which had been kept a secret from the others. The small pit was the one where we had seen the tracks the week before. It was very significant, to say the least, that some information was not shared between these friends. Over the years, I slowly understood that reality. Dad was not surprised and managed to park the Nash far away from the pit. Taking the backpack and putting it on his back, Uncle Lee put on his gloves and handed me mine. He reached into the trunk and carefully selected a number one-and-three-quarter square-jawed trap. With everything in order, we all walked slowly toward the trap location. The extremes my uncle took were mandatory, but also necessary as far as he was concerned. Dad watched diligently when my uncle informed both of us that he was going to show me a fox set he developed and had never shown anyone. My father was fascinated with this technique and I was told I was going to make the entire set myself, and if it wasn't right, we were going to stay until it was. Trust me when I say that set was and will remain a family secret that produced foxes for over three generations.

Uncle Lee helped set the trap and pounded in the wooden oak stake. Each small detail was explained slowly and I attempted to perform the instructions with some insecurity. I totally understood the instruction, yet fumbled often and had to recover as expected. Uncle kept his patience and my father was enthralled by this attempt to make my first fox set. After several failures, the set was finished to uncle's specifications with the exception of applying bait, urine and the secret which I have never divulged. Wiping away tracks and other human evidence, the three generations walked back to the Nash with swaggers that came from macho expressions of a sense of accomplishment. The day had been filled to the brim and exhaustion was overtaken by the reality that everyone had participated in a special event that can never be captured again. We were all inspired by nature and wildlife, which allowed the spiritual aspect of life to soak into the tradition of our family. While we rode toward home, a unique calmness was prevalent with discussion about the Grey Ghost, and I was finally asked if I had smelled him and answered with conviction.

I explained that he smelled different than other bucks and I was surprised by his size. Uncle asked about the smell difference and I replied he smelled stronger and the odor of stale pond mud which was evident, like when I played around the ponds catching frogs. I also informed uncle and Dad that Freckles would smell sour after his hunts, and it was similar to the smell of the Grey Ghost. I felt somewhat intimidated, but continued my attempt to explain how the Grey Ghost knew everyone by their smell. Uncle asked with interest what I meant. I informed him that each old codger had a smell distinct to them. Mutt smelled like Carter Hall and Weasel smelled like Prince Albert, while uncle had the aroma of Yankee Girl. I also informed dad that he smelled like cigarettes. I realized that this information was soaking in slowly and I knew the wheels were turning. Dad wanted to know more about my observations and wondered how I learned about deer behavior.

I explained that during hunting season I would sit in an old apple tree way down the Dusty Trail when hunters were in the woods. I continued when the bucks would congregate around the orchard and frog pond to avoid danger. They were always aware of my presence and weren't afraid. I offered more information by saying the Grey Ghost knew where these codgers were while they attempted to bag him. It was that statement which sparked my uncle with an assertive lecture about my not knowing what I was talking about. The lecture was stopped by Dad when he gracefully mentioned that he felt I was perceptive in my observations. He asked what the deer did while I observed them. I answered the only thing that disturbed them was quick movement and a hunter wandering into the area. They would slowly work their way behind the hunter. "Ray you're right, we need to rethink our approach to getting the Grey Ghost." My uncle sat quietly, deep in thought.

CHAPTER 13

Memories of Family Traditions

As we drove into our drive, my exhaustion was evident. My uncle was a bit crotchety, so I tried not to aggravate him in an attempt to avoid disputes. My father noticed Uncle Lee's mood and suggested he eat and take a well-deserved nap. He grunted reluctantly in agreement.

After answering several questions from my mom about the day, I grabbed a pillow and lay down on the floor with Freckles. I started falling asleep with a sense of well-being and recalled each moment spent with the old codgers with fondness. The smell of Freckles was soothing, and it was evident that an addiction to fox trapping was gradually seeping into my blood. With emotional feelings toward my family and old codger friends, I fell asleep with relaxed anticipation for meeting later at the store. My excitement was internal regarding our checking sets in the morning. That ritual followed me for over sixty-five years and it always managed to give me feelings of peace and excitement.

Both Dad and I were awakened by Mom with help from my sister for supper, which consisted of venison tenderloins with mashed potatoes and gravy. The vegetables were from our garden and had been canned by mom and sister. I remember the details of that supper, since it remains my favorite meal to this day. The family traditions were always consistent and every detail was filled with love and occasionally some unexpected treat, like fresh apple pie and ice cream served for dessert. Looking back to that day with fondness, I realize nothing remains the same in the name of progress. There will always be a longing in my heart for days of such comfort and security brought about by these traditions.

With time approaching for our nightly trip to the liquor store, Dad injected a comment regarding Mutt's health. He and Mom seemed concerned, which made me uncomfortable. While leaving the house, the weather was cold, with a very light rain. I was informed that nights like these caused animals to move, which would increase our chances. Getting into our old Chevy, the dialogue was kept to the Grey Ghost and how this deer was causing more intrigue by the year. I mentioned that it was evident that they needed to understand that the Grey Ghost knew everyone by name and smell. Dad laughed and indicated that I was right, but said, "It would probably take an act of Congress to convince the old codgers about my theory." It was then that he wanted me to shut up and not to inject my thoughts unless asked by Uncle Lee.

Dad added that he believed I was onto something which could very easily help in bagging that old buck. He openly commented that I had surprised him with the detail of my observations along the Dusty Trail.

With that endorsement, I felt significant and my ego had been massaged to a level of acceptance. My dad's confidence in me was very uplifting and I appreciated his approval.

CHAPTER 14

Valuable Life Lessons

Walking down Main Street toward the store, I noticed that Leo was crossing the street. He was waving for us to wait for him, which we did. Leo was excited by our sighting of the Grey Ghost and he seemed full of energy. I was happy that his mood was elevated and he appeared more comfortable in his behavior.

I noticed Walking Charlie was headed in our direction and when he got in front of me I said hello. Charlie looked at me and just said, "I don't know you," and kept walking. Both Dad and Leo laughed out loud and Charlie yelled back, "I heard that and I'm going to tell Leon Richards on all of you."

Dad poked Leo and replied, "We're in trouble now, because Charlie won't forget." Walking with Leo was different since his mood was a bit friskier and he seemed much happier.

The three of us walked into the store and with the bells ringing, there was a strange feeling that there was something different about the atmosphere in the office. Our friend Mutt wasn't here yet. While we were removing our jackets and hats, Simon echoed his concern with Mutt's health and everyone agreed with his observation. It was during this conversation between the codgers that I learned that Mutt had a serious heart condition. I knew very little about medical problems, but I comprehended their concern.

The store door opened and the bells rang and to everyone's surprise, Walking Charlie walked straight to the office area. Dad was nervous, and for that matter so was Leo. Charlie stood by my uncle and in his excitement told him that the three of us laughed at him and he wanted Uncle Lee to call the cops. That's when my uncle got up slowly and put his hand on Charlie's shoulder for comfort. I was amazed at how gentle and comforting my uncle handled Charlie's mood. Uncle Lee softly explained that we had been laughing about a movie. He then asked Charlie to sit down and to my surprise, he sat next to me with some apprehension noticeable. Then Uncle Lee introduced me to Charlie and with respect, Charlie stood up to shake my hand. I slowly stood and put out my small hand, which he gently took as he slowly said, "I didn't know you then, but I know you now." Charlie turned to Uncle Lee and said not to call the cops.

Sitting back down, Charlie looked around the office and asked for a piece of candy. That's when Uncle Lee opened the desk drawer, which housed a bag of hard peppermint candies, and offered Charlie three, which he unwrapped and put in his mouth. With a mouth filled with candy, he thanked Uncle Lee and turned and walked into the cold, damp evening.

Uncle Lee stood up and shook his head in disbelief. Looking everyone in the eyes, he reminded them that Charlie always got nervous and confused around this time of year. They all agreed and realized Charlie's dilemma. That was the moment Dad issued a concern for Charlie's future during the coming winter. Leo suggested a need for someone to check on Charlie occasionally and offered to help if needed. These old men were concerned and willing to help if possible. Even at my age, I learned a very valuable lesson. I was reminded by these codgers the value of Sunday school and attending church. This encounter was difficult for me to digest completely, but I was grateful for my relationship with my family and new friends.

With the mood recovered from Walking Charlie's performance, the subject quickly focused on the Grey Ghost. A tremendous amount of energy and time had apparently been spent on plans to outsmart the huge whitetail. While I listened intently, my father was in my corner and stayed out of the discussion. Two interesting events regarding that deer still stir memories of Simon's and Weasel's near-misses. Simon had taken a position near the end of the swamp during a morning watch after an eight-inch snow fall. He had seated himself properly, regarding wind direction, and sat for two hours without moving a muscle. The temperature was twenty-eight degrees and he started to get cold and damp. Simon recalled watching two does wander past and expected the Grey Ghost to follow, since it was during the rut. After several minutes he had gotten impatient and decided to wander around to check for tracks. When he got up and turned around and looked in his tracks, the Grey Ghost track was in his; that old buck had walked within twenty feet of him. That old buck had stood in Simon's track and had performed his morning duties just to insult him.

The other account was from Weasel as he had wandered into the swamp about a hundred yards in just before daylight. He had picked a spot where he could see clearly around a hundred yards in three shooting lanes. He sat until ten in the morning and then decided to call it a day. While getting up, that buck bolted from behind a blowdown that was less then twenty yards from Weasel. Apparently, that buck had allowed Weasel to sit down for his watch and the Grey Ghost had watched him for the entire time! There were similar stories offered by everyone, which excited my curiosity. There was no question that the Grey Ghost was king of the swamp. My uncle wasn't offering any input except that his primary focus was that old buck for the coming deer season, which opened in a week.

The subject got back to trapping and it was decided that there was no need for everyone to join in the checking of my sets. They all predicted success and wanted Uncle Lee to call with the results. The reason for not joining in our line was each of them wanted to get sets out themselves. Uncle Lee seemed pleased by that decision and rubbed his chin, which indicated some ulterior motive. I had spent enough time with my uncle to read his body language. A customer came in and there was snow falling and it appeared to be sticking. No one expected this snow, but my uncle issued a prediction which aroused my excitement. He predicted four beaver, no mink and a few rats. Simon replied, "What about foxes?"

My uncle replied, "We'll see." Dad poked me in the ribs, indicating affection, and attempted to remain disengaged in this conversation. I was slowly learning about secrets among friends. I was being introduced to male characteristics regarding protecting their territory. These lessons were a contradiction of honesty and everything I had learned in Sunday school about fibbing. I knew Dad would be prepared to answer my questions regarding avoiding or circumventing the truth.

Slowly, all the men stood and excused themselves, knowing the next day was going to be work related to putting their traps out. They were excited about my trapping introduction, but seemed anxious to get their own trap lines started. After they all left, my uncle locked the door and returned to his chair. Sitting down with a relaxed effort, his eyes sparkled and his chin was clinched with some tension. He started wringing his hands, which indicated he was very intense.

He slowly gave my dad some indication about his theory regarding utilizing my nose for opening day of deer season.

My father protected my integrity when he told uncle that he had felt that he hadn't believed his son regarding his nose for deer. Uncle Lee stood up and with his hands on his hips, replied he was reluctant to believe, but if I could prove my power, it would be the answer to the Grey Ghost.

I decided to break my silence, and looking at my father, explained that there was a ten-point wandering around the frog pond down the Dusty Trail. He seemed surprised and asked why I never told anyone about those deer. I hadn't expected that question and replied I was cheering for the deer. My uncle got upset with that answer, which I'm sure threatened his plans for utilizing my nose. It was apparent listening to Dad and uncle that my nose value was gaining more worth by the minute. With some difficulty, I tried to explain that my nose ability wasn't the only answer. Other modifications would have to be accomplished. My uncle got really angry. He raised his voice when he asked what in the hell I knew about deer hunting. I reacted by saying, "Its one thing to smell the deer and another thing to get a good shot."

He angrily said, "You smell him and leave the rest to me."

I reacted to this verbal attack with, "The whole thing stinks, and you should realize that if human contamination is the secret to successful trapping animals, then why don't you understand what I'm saying about pipe and cigarette smoke?" That's when Dad stepped in and was shocked by my verbal explanation he felt had attacked Uncle Lee's ego. I understood the problem and offered a solution to this stand-off. I told both of them that if they wanted my nose, I needed them to listen to my demands. They were both shocked and visually upset with my tenacity and standing my ground with conviction. I asked a simple question that sat both of them down. "It's my nose, and if your so intent on using it, then I should be able to determine some of the details surrounding this attempt to outsmart the Grey Ghost!"

Neither my dad or uncle were prepared for my stand and were speechless. I continued by explaining that I had been listening to everyone for weeks and I appreciated everything that had taken place. It was surprisingly interesting and fun. I said, "The problem tonight is you're not willing to listen like you always expect me to. It's just like school, the teacher is always right, even when she doesn't really understand or comprehend the question. It always angers me when you tell the truth and adults still won't listen." I was on the verge of tears and my chin started quivering, revealing my vulnerable emotional state.

My father assumed his parental role by trying to defuse the emotion. He attempted to negotiate a compromise. But his answer to this unique problem was shot down by Uncle Lee, who was stubborn and had dug in his heels. I also refused to budge about my nose and told Dad to forget everything I told them. My uncle went into the bathroom and after returning to his chair took a deep breath, indicating his frustration. My father was scolding me about respect and I started to cry. I had never felt such emotional pain over a confrontation when I knew I was right and yet still was expected to give in.

Fortunately, a knock on the store's door stopped this vicious circle. My father went to investigate and yelled to uncle about throwing him the keys to unlock the door. I could hear high heels and I smelled Martha's perfume. I tried to say hello, but only managed a whimper. Martha realized she had walked into a hornet's nest and responded with, "What is going on?" My uncle explained in some detail about the nose issue and how I had taken a stand that had irritated him. He also informed her that it was probably not even possible for anyone to smell deer. She seemed concerned and handed me a Kleenex. I stole a glance at her. Wow, there was no doubt she was gorgeous with her hair piled high, and once again she was wearing the fox jacket. Her high heel boots were covered with snow and she appeared stately and elegant. With an attitude that was caring and understanding, she sat down next to my dad. She calmly directed her conversation to them and left me out.

Both Dad and uncle were shocked by her injection of her theory regarding the standoff. Martha got in front of them and in typical teacher fashion, pointed her finger at both of them. With her finger pointed at my uncle, she harshly spoke with conviction and reminded him how pig-headed he could be. She continued lecturing all of us about negotiation skills, then stopped in the middle of her statement and didn't finish her thought. Sitting down again, she apologized for interfering but wanted us to realize it was not impossible to keep peace with three pig-headed members of the same family. "You're all acting like kindergarten kids and you should be ashamed by this nonsense." Martha continued, "Ray has an excuse, but Lee obviously never learned he didn't have all the answers. My God, you three are certainly out of the same mold. No wonder the bitterness is so entrenched." She reminded my uncle that his stubbornness had caused problems in the past and he of all people should understand and appreciate where Ray was coming from. Never before in my life had I seen my uncle or Dad looking so beat and a bit embarrassed. Martha explained the odor problem and knew I was correct. "You guys have always had success with deer, but you're up against the smartest buck you've encountered." Martha asked my father if he believed me and wanted to know if there was any reason for me to fib. He told Martha that he felt I could smell deer, and as far as he knew I wouldn't have lied.

It was then I reminded everyone that my sister could also smell deer and that was enough evidence to prove my point. Martha was perplexed and asked if that was true. Both adults said "Yes," and a light went on.

Uncle Lee was grasping for excuses and failed miserably. He had only one option, which he found difficult. He was forced to admit he was wrong on several counts. I felt sorry for both Dad and uncle but realized I was also a bit unrealistic. Martha started to laugh and referred to my confronting Fat Earl and that they had been pleased by that stand. Martha asked, "What would make you think Ray wouldn't challenge any subject he felt strongly about? You guys can't have it both ways." I was captivated by Martha's good looks, but her temperament was really smooth. Martha was queen of the liquor store that night. There were no formal apologies except from Martha, when she graciously referred to having loved Uncle Lee for fifty years regardless of his faults. She also said that her reason for stopping was to ask permission to join us in the morning while we checked our traps. My uncle needed some moral support, especially from Martha. It all made sense to me now. My uncle always seemed a bit unnerved when she was present. I was right, Uncle Lee loved Martha, too.

The realization of my Uncle's obsession with the Grey Ghost was elevated when he opened the desk drawer that housed the peppermint candies and reached inside. A pencil sketch was mounted and framed which allowed me to feel a renewed purpose. The sketch was of the Grey Ghost standing on the edge of the small stream. It was an exact portrait of that deer. I will always cherish his ability to capture his emotions by sketching significant subjects with such detail. He pulled out another which portrayed me making my first fox set. The sketch was so lifelike it evoked strong loving feelings. That sketch was the most generous gift I ever received. I have always relished that depiction. Feelings of love flowed and to be frank, it was a gift from my uncle's heart. He had sketched that likeness that afternoon. I was determined to help my old uncle bag that monster whitetail. The whole evening had been filled with such a roller coaster ride of emotions that we were all exhausted. Walking into the snowfall was refreshing and clean, which was needed by all of us.

Emotional days like these allowed me the luxury and realization that pride and ignorance could really cause problems in any relationship. I was young and inexperienced regarding confrontation with loved ones. Within that conflict I learned some valuable lessons about human behavior. I understood the trials and tribulations that I was going to confront periodically in the future. I recalled a Sunday school lesson regarding caring and sharing with openness and honesty. The only thing they missed was the tremendous complex issue of egos and how protective we all are regarding our life experiences. After all these years, conflict was always a result of fear of being viewed as being weak. That truth was learned that night and has held true my entire life.

In trying to avoid an argument between me and Uncle Lee, my dad was having difficulty discussing plans for a time to check our sets in the morning, and eight was decided upon. Martha appeared subdued due to the emotional transformation she had witnessed. My uncle appeared tired from the internal exhaustion my smelling deer had created.

The temperature was below freezing allowing the snow to accumulate on the old Chevy and for the first snowfall it seemed early and much heavier than normal. Very little dialogue was shared, indicating enough was enough. Martha and uncle were talking about her new truck in a futile attempt to put living conflict back into perspective.

My father explained during the ride home how uncharacteristic the disagreement between myself and uncle had been, making it tough to diffuse. He went on describing my personality changes and my uncle's problem accepting my normal maturation process. Dad replied he had felt a bit angry with my delivery, which was not my typical behavior. Dad told me that my experience with deer observation had complicated the plans my uncle had devised. Reaching and patting my hand for reassurance, the whole situation about the Grey Ghost seemed more complex than ever. "The problem was that your assertiveness was a bit extreme, which made your uncle uncomfortable. It's been a very long time since he has been challenged with details he wasn't prepared to accept, even though he knew you were correct in your observations." I tried to understand, but to be honest, fell short of comprehending this issue. "Ray, it's very true when you hear it's difficult to teach an old dog new tricks." That was the first time I ever heard that statement, and it helped make the conflict more comforting and understandable.

The snow was falling at a steady rate and since the leaves weren't all off the trees, the white birches were drooping under the stress. It sort of symbolized my own weary body. My dad seemed preoccupied, which prompted me to ask if I had been completely wrong. He shook his head no. Then his reaction toward the events of the evening helped clarify the mixed emotions that had been displayed. "It's normal, but difficult for a man of uncle's age to admit his failures and character flaws, especially from you at your age," he said. "Understand it wasn't personal, it was only a display of his vulnerability. One of uncle's faults has always been his stubbornness, and he usually regrets this behavior after he thinks about the ramifications and repercussions that characteristic can cause. You're similar in that aspect, but you're much more compassionate. Everything will be okay after a good night's sleep."

Walking toward the porch in five inches of wet snow, my father asked what I had learned about trapping and wanted my reaction. I explained my intrigue and interest in fox sets and said that was really interesting. Smiling, he told me he wasn't surprised and had anticipated that answer. He loved fox hunting and hounds like my uncle, but couldn't do it justice with work and family responsibility. I simply nodded and thanked him for not being angry. Walking into the kitchen, we were met by Mom, who seemed worried about it being so late and with the heavy snowfall, thought we had gone into a ditch. She helped take my jacket and hat to be hung next to the wood stove. The undercurrent was evident between my parents as I fumbled with washing up for bed. I overheard Dad explaining some detail about the evening and both parents laughed when my father said it was a good thing I had my mother's stubbornness and his good looks. The humor was badly needed as I slowly walked the stairs looking forward to the comfort of my bed. Pulling the blanket under my chin, I was visualizing each set with anticipation, which remained a characteristic of my nightly ritual. After my parents left to go downstairs I said good night to my sister who was sleeping and thought fondly about my best friend, Freckles. I really missed that one-eyed hound that evening.

The morning was greeted reluctantly until I remember the purpose for being awakened by Dad. I looked out the window and the winter wonderland seemed so clean and fresh I felt great and ready to go. Glancing toward the shed, I noticed Martha's truck was behind the Nash and was covered with snow. That could only mean one of two things. Maybe her brand-new truck was broken or she was there really early. I was obviously wrong about both theories. I also noticed that my uncle's hunting jacket and pants were hung on the deer hanging rack, airing. I was called for breakfast and heard several people talking with excitement. Running down the stairs to investigate my mom was hugging Martha and saying hello. Uncle Lee was smiling from ear-to-ear. With a sense of purpose I seemed confused by all the happiness. Surprised and taken aback, I stumbled with words but eventually just blurted that she was really pretty and my uncle should shave more often. Hugging me with respect and love, she told me that it was my job to remind uncle about his facial hair and contamination. Everyone laughed and breakfast was served on mom's good dishes that were saved for special occasions. I was excited and referred to the heavy snowfall and then my uncle responded with it will help the trapping and give us an opportunity to investigate the Grey Ghost's movements.

With dishes put away, everyone started getting dressed appropriately for our adventure of checking my sets for the first time. The mood was elevated and the events of the previous evening were forgotten and buried. Life was happily back to normal.

Walking outside with my entire new hunting outfit, I ran out back and hugged my hounds, especially Freckles. I whispered in his ear that I was going to get a fox of my own. Running to the Nash, I was seated next to Martha while Dad and Uncle Lee expressed the feelings of anticipation that accompanied checking a trap line. Martha smiled and reached out and patted my hands that were clenched in excitement.

CHAPTER 15

The Keys to the Future

The snow accumulation was about six inches deep, making driving difficult, since the roads hadn't been plowed yet. I was captivated by the mystical attitude this eventful morning captured. My uncle was alive with enthusiasm after a good night's sleep and probably never anticipated sharing this opening day with three significant loved ones. I'm positive this adventure couldn't have been visualized or created any more perfectly. Dad was concentrating on his driving while Martha hummed some song she obviously liked.

Martha was dressed in very fashionable hunting attire for ladies. She was so striking her presence was comfortable, which allowed me the luxury to enjoy it. I also realized the attraction my uncle must have experienced and why he was captivated. She was so pretty it was difficult not to stare at her without being obvious and rude.

Getting closer to Clayton's farm, my heart and soul were transfixed by the peace and serenity Mother Nature had created for us to enjoy. I was relishing my first opening day of trapping season. There are very few moments in a young boy's life that stand out so vividly in memory with such detail. Driving up to the locked gate, my father surprisingly turned off the old Nash and sat back in his seat to witness and enjoy the entire wintry scene. This snowfall had created feelings of peace and tranquility that encompassed the meadows and hedge-rows that graphically identified this well-managed farm. Dad turned his head and looked at me with a caring expression. He then turned in my uncle's direction and replied that he had never seen snow on opening day of trapping season, and that it must be an omen. My uncle took off his wire-framed glasses, which he seldom wore, and wiped the lenses clean with his handkerchief. Turning toward me, he handed me the keys to the gate. He told me it was my line and it was only fitting for me to unlock and open the gate to memories I would never forget. He obviously realized the transformation I was about to experience. Then, without warning, he reached back, grabbed my hand and said, "This is only the beginning of your life that will be filled with endless memories." He continued, "God willing, may this continue our family traditions. Ray, these are the keys to your future; it's time to unlock that reality." Martha softly replied that it was only fitting that my uncle and I go open the gate, since it's being handed off with the past and future generations to encapsulate this lifestyle.

Taking the keys, I told both Dad and uncle I felt all four of us needed to open the gate, and Martha responded that my suggestion was appropriate and if I wanted that memory it needed fulfilling. We all got out and walked toward the gate, and I remember how the snow felt under my new packs. I walked slowly with Uncle Lee at my side and Martha and Dad watching from a few steps behind. Reaching for the lock and wrestling with the key, my uncle reached down and reminded me that the key only went in one way and showed tolerance in his explanation. After the lock was opened and the chain wrapped around the metal frame, my uncle told me to open the gate pushing forward, since it was a symbol of walking into the future. "Don't ever close a gate by pulling it toward you, because it's always bad luck," he explained.

With the gate open, I was filled with feelings that allowed graphic visions of a complex emotional realization that was transpiring. My uncle suggested we check the beaver pond first and Dad struggled finding the tote road, but he managed. The mood was elevated when several grouse flushed from out of a hedgerow and Martha reminded Uncle Lee she hadn't had grouse that fall and blamed her lack of enthusiasm for hunting grouse after her bird dog passed away. Pulling the old Nash around a corner, the beaver pond was only around another bend, avoiding several large boulders, making the bend the most beautiful spectacle I can remember, that rendered everyone speechless. The pond water was black as coal, without a ripple. All the trees were laden with snow which was reflecting back on the water.

Then my dad said, "There is a God and for those who don't believe, they never witnessed anything this gorgeous." No one said a word. We were totally transfixed by the peace and serenity of this small pond that represented a mystic vision of wonder created by Mother Nature and the reality of creation. I have thousands of visual memories, but I cannot recall witnessing another moment so graphically.

Uncle broke the silence with, "It's moments like this which have always motivated my need to spend time in the wilderness." He continued by saying he could see two beaver tails, which indicated success. He opened the car door and reminded everyone it was time to get to work and check the other sets. With all of us out and getting our bearings, Dad asked if I remembered where the other beaver sets were. I said I thought so and he suggested putting on my waders.

With my waders on, I waited for Uncle Lee to put his on before attempting to drag the beaver to shore. That first experience of seeing a beaver up close generated mixed emotions. They were ugly with huge teeth and their tails intrigued me. I had a million questions, but was reminded there would be time for that later after we got all the catches bagged and loaded into the box built for success in the trunk of the Nash. We had four adult beaver, which was exciting; however, these sets had to be remade. Dad was working slowly and instructed me again about proper beaver sets. The experience my dad had regarding this effort indicated his own expertise, which reminded me that he knew more regarding trapping than I realized. I guess he wanted my uncle to be in charge of my education without any contradictions or confusion relative to not stepping on my uncle's toes. The beaver were tended to, so mink and rat sets were next. All of us walked toward the two streams with relaxed anticipation except for my hyper internal curiosity. These sets produced six muskrats and one large male mink. I reacted with satisfaction, which pleased the adults.

The sets were remade by everyone, including Martha. At the time, I knew Martha was also an experienced trapper, which somehow didn't fit her appearance. Stepping onto the traps for setting she was comfortable with this task which indicated her involvement with my uncle in the past. After remaking the water sets, it was time to check our fox sets which piqued my interest even more. There was something about foxes and the intense methods it took for success which seemed more interesting than water trapping. After getting back into the Nash and heading toward the meadows and cornfields, everyone also seemed more excited. The three sets made by the codgers produced one large coon in Leo's set. It was during remaking that set when my uncle suggested I remake the set utilizing the information he had shown me the day before. Everything went well except for some minor changes uncle made explaining as he went. During the ride to-ward the last set, my father referred to the profit that had been made based on the prior year's fur prices. I was all ears after hearing his estimate. The reality of trapping reward also came from cold clean cash. Profit was a serious motivator for serious trappers and I learned a valuable lesson on the premise of catching and selling the pelts for money. My uncle stayed away from that discussion due to my mom's requirement that I was to get some share of the profits. Thinking back, it's humorous by today's standards, but back then it was significant. I wondered what it would feel like to buy twenty-five baseball cards at a time. This trapping had more rewards than I had previously imagined.

My attention was brought back to the mission at hand when Martha asked what sets were left to check. Uncle replied, "Just one, around the next corner." Dad seemed relaxed and satisfied with our take thus far and for that matter, so was Uncle Lee. I suddenly felt apprehension regarding the special type set that was a proven fox taker. Rounding the bend, the entire attitude changed when a huge red fox started jumping in the set I had made on my own! Uncle Lee yelled, "It's an omen, like you said, Leon. Stop the damn car and let Ray observe his first red!" With the snow in the background, this red fox was so beautiful I had no visible reaction, but the emotional feelings seemed dreamlike. Martha said she had never seen such a magnificent fox in her life.

Then Dad added, "That's the biggest and most beautiful fox I've ever seen." Getting out for a better view, my insides turned-upside down and I started shaking with excitement.

A great deal of time was spent enjoying this moment, and when I looked toward uncle, he removed his glasses and wiped his eyes. "My God, that's the old dog fox I pinched two years ago I bet he's missing a toe," he said. "How in the hell did we outsmart him?"

I just uttered, "There was no contamination."

He laughed and remarked, "You know something, Ray? You're absolutely right. Let's put this fox down and remake the set, because we have a lot of work ahead of us."

While I carried the fox toward the Nash, I was amazed by the variety of colors that were blended into his coat. The reds were enhanced with some black and blond hairs that accentuated the black legs glistening like velvet in the sun. His tail was primarily red with the tip having extremely black hair that ran about six inches toward the tip of his tail, and the last six inches were completely white. This tail was so bushy it appeared fake. It was during everyone's observation about this magnificent fox my dad asked if anyone knew a taxidermist that could do justice to this specimen. Martha remarked she knew only one she trusted, but he was expensive and lived in the next small town, called Madrid. She said she had seen several mounts, but this man's work was world-famous because he specialized in fox taxidermy. Both my dad and uncle agreed that this fox should be mounted regardless of the cost because it represented everything good about the family traditions regarding foxes. The day was complete, with more fur than I thought possible. Dad suggested we drive over and drop off the fox for mounting, which everyone agreed to. Uncle visualized a mount that gave the fox an appearance of being relaxed without looking aggressive. I knew and understood his vision for this mount. The details with the taxidermist were made and Martha put down the deposit since dad and uncle weren't prepared.

After arriving home and showing off our success to mom and my sister, the job of skinning and fleshing needed to be done. While I watched this process, I wondered how often my uncle and Dad had preformed this dirty, smelly job. The mink and rats were easy, but those ugly beavers were another issue. Martha had gone into the house and uncle suggested I go ask for lunch, which I did, and she was already heating soup and making venison tenderloin sandwiches.

CHAPTER 16

Martha's Story

Sitting at the familiar small kitchen table having a bowl of soup and sandwich with Martha, I recall trying to understand the complications that had prevented my uncle and her from marrying. This small kitchen area had all of my grandmother's kitchen utensils and necessities required for feeding a family of ten children. As I looked around, there were pots and pans hung over the wood-burning cooking stove. This kitchen appeared to have been left in the same condition my grandmother had always kept it. There were several metal frying pans and lids sitting on top of the old stove and I remembered the ceramic baked bean pot that always sat in the warming oven and it was still there. That brown pot was usually filled with either baked beans and salt pork or venison stew when available. I had very fond memories of my grandmother. She had always been happy and gracious, even after she became ill. She eventually passed away when I was six. I asked Martha if she had ever met my grandmother and she meekly nodded yes and offered, "Ray, your uncle's sister and your grandmother always felt she had been in the way of your uncle Lee and I. That wasn't really the only reason we weren't able to marry, but it was a serious factor."

As I ate my sandwich, Martha pulled up a chair and sat down to enjoy a cup of tea. For some strange reason, she started explaining the entire sequence of events which had transpired during this long-term relationship that had gone on for over fifty years. Even at my age, I was transfixed by this conversation, so I listened intently.

Martha started at the beginning, with no reluctance in describing the relationship in detail. Apparently, her father had owned a successful sawmill and several homes and property that he rented. Both of her parents were very protective and staunch Methodists. Her dad sponsored several sports teams such as a hockey team named the Scarlet Stars and a baseball team called the Scarlet Wiz Kids. She had oftentimes noticed my uncle and wondered why he never seemed to notice her. She recalled her father mentioning she needed a new beaver blanket for her horse carriage and had ordered it from uncle, who was only sixteen at the time. He had already established a reputation for being a tremendous outdoors man and it was common knowledge that he was very solitary with striking good looks. My uncle apparently wasn't impressed by her dad, which irritated him. Uncle never treated her father the way he expected. Martha said her dad was full of himself and to be honest, "My family, including myself, were guilty of feeling a bit superior. We had money and lived comfortably and resided in a very modern huge home for those days." Martha went on explaining that her dad had tried to hire my uncle to work at his sawmill, but couldn't convince him. She said, "Your uncle had a reputation for indifference due to his independence and love of freedom to enjoy his passions in the outdoors."

Martha recalled going to a hockey game around Christmastime because her dad was interested in seeing how his money was being spent. She recalled getting all dressed up hoping to attract some response from my uncle. Martha recalled sitting in the bleachers with blankets and wearing heavy warm boots and leather gloves tucked into a fox fur hand warmer muff. She said, "I knew most of the players on the team and they all seemed to know I was present. Sitting with my parents and a girlfriend from school, we were sipping hot tea trying to stay warm. When the teams were warming up, I realized your uncle wasn't there, and I was a bit discouraged. All of my preparation to attract your uncle seemed fruitless, and with cold feet and ears, I remember thinking and wondering why I had bothered to primp without any results. The game was just about ready to start when the gate at the end of the rink opened and your uncle skated onto the ice. I was captivated by his smooth coordinated skating skills. He showed agility that was effortless. Your uncle looked into the stands briefly and our eyes met. It was obvious he wasn't comfortable, he just looked away casually.

I knew instantly we were connected, regardless of how hard he tried to avoid the chemistry."

She continued, "My mom asked my dad who number five was, and he remarked, 'It's a kid from Skunk Ridge with a cocky personality that needs trimming.' My mom poked me and just winked. She had felt my interest change as soon as Lee hit the ice. Your uncle was a tremendous hockey player, yet he seemed very distant and unassuming, which was very attractive, and that characteristic is still interesting today. After the hockey game, my dad went into the player's shed and walked out with his beaver blanket, which was trimmed with fox tails. It was obvious my dad was angry and my mother asked why he was mad. He exclaimed, 'The cocky kid wanted his money before he gave me the blanket. For some reason he didn't trust my word about paying him on payday. That cocky kid informed me he didn't work at the mill, so payday was when I took the blanket.' That was the beginning of their standoff. My father never tolerated anyone who challenged him, especially a young, handsome but arrogant sixteen-year-old. The mystery that surrounded Lee made him difficult to ignore and honestly every girl in town would comment on your uncle's looks, coupled with his apparent disinterest in social events. My girlfriends always seemed infatuated with your uncle, so I tried to appear disinterested."

"One afternoon after school, I was being walked home by a male friend. Your uncle walked out of the woods near the path my friend and I were walking on. Your uncle had a shotgun slung over his shoulder and reached down and patted his hound. He glanced our way and sauntered in our direction, whistling as he walked with confidence. Just before we were to pass, my male friend mentioned that your uncle was always wandering in the woods with that old hound. My uncle heard that comment and just tipped his cap, winked at me and that was the moment I realized how infatuated I was with that handsome, cocky, self-assured man that seemed heads and tails above any other man I had ever known. I knew there was some difficulty contacting your uncle and started devising a plan to entice him into a meeting he couldn't refuse. I spent days trying to manipulate the means for such a meeting. I felt the only way was to admit that if you couldn't beat them, then you had to join them on their ground. Understand your uncle Lee had quit school, even though he was a good student. His problem seemed related to a conflict between studies and his love for hunting, fishing and trapping. At his age, jobs were available, yet he made pretty good money living off the land. He was always in great shape from splitting wood and playing sports with his friends. He always had a few foxhounds and even back then his dogs had great reputations. He had a way with hounds just like he did with the ladies."

"The reason I couldn't get close enough to meet him was due to the fact that he was either in the woods or hanging with his male buddies. You need to remember all this was taking place long before your grandmother was married and had her ten children." I confessed to Martha that it was hard for me to think about uncle at sixteen years old. The answer I received was a bit unnerving when she told me I was going to be the spitting image of Lee when I was sixteen and she believed my disposition was also going to be similar. She patted my hand and said, "Ray, that's a compliment. You two have the same smile and grin and your eyes sparkle just like his when you're excited. If I had to guess, you're already starting to evolve into being captivated by nature and wildlife."

Martha continued explaining that she knew Mutt from school and used him to set up a meeting with Uncle Lee. Her plan was to get Mutt to ask uncle if he could provide a red fox scarf with matching hat and earmuffs. I remember thinking what a clever plan she had devised.

Her plan worked as expected, and she was to meet my uncle after school Friday in the location they had met on the path near the woods. She recalled how nervous she was and admitted she was a bit reluctant knowing how her dad felt abut Uncle Lee. After school she admitted hanging around to avoid company on the way down the path. Martha continued, "When the coast was clear, I walked excitedly for our meeting. Your uncle was waiting and appeared very nervous, which helped my confidence. Getting closer, I recall his chin was clenched and he reached down to pat his hound, whose name was Sport. That old black and tan walked toward me and your uncle called him back."

"I said, 'Hello Lee, I want to talk to you about a fox scarf hat and ear muffs. Can you provide them for me?' He looked me straight in the eyes and told me he wouldn't have come if he couldn't. He was guarded, and with his usual carefree manner, asked if they were for me personally or just a gift. Both of us were aware of the energy we were creating, so I asked if he wanted to walk and discuss this transaction. That broke the tension and he elaborated on the entire process it would take, which would cost some serious money. Lee explained that he had enough prime foxes, but they needed tanning, so he would have an old Mohawk Indian friend tan them and his wife could do the sewing required. As we walked he reached into his hunting jacket and removed a small tablet and pencil. He started sketching and after a few minutes he handed it to me and asked if I approved of his ideas regarding the scarf and hat, since ear-muffs were ear muffs. I was amazed and a bit intimidated by his talent and was even more surprised when he handed me a sketch of me wearing the three items being discussed. With some insecurity your uncle asked if I approved and he felt fox fur would compliment my personality and great looks. Needless to say that was just the beginning. It was your uncle who suggested walking me home because he realized how late it was getting and thought my parents would be worried. That surprised me and really made a huge impression. Walking slowly, he indicated that I would probably have to get a fitting for the hat, and he would set up the time. I was so infatuated with his grasp of these details my whole previous attraction was compounded twofold. He was smart, artistic and polite. These were characteristics I hadn't expected. I thought he would be a bit crude and very abrupt, but none of that was apparent."

CHAPTER 17

Standing Up for What's Right

Martha got up for more tea, and that's when my uncle and dad opened the kitchen door to have a late lunch. They both suggested that I go observe the beaver that had been placed on the stretching boards. They wanted me to see the proper method of stretching beaver, and my uncle said we had three blanket beaver and one super blanket. The explanation for determining the difference would be discussed after they ate. Everyone was tired from the events of the day, but it was discussed fondly. Obviously, the fox was the highlight of the day, because foxes were the family obsession. While Dad had a beer and uncle some tea, he started a conversation regarding the Grey Ghost. Martha suggested they both needed to listen to her and I before trying to plan anything radical. I was actually surprised by her assertiveness, not knowing what she was going to say in regard to her ideas. I was disappointed about being interrupted during our conversation about her plan to attract uncle, but I knew we would continue at a more appropriate time. Since the Grey Ghost was the subject at hand, I wanted to hear Martha's ideas, and I also knew I was the only one interested.

That was typical behavior for both uncle and dad. They usually ignored Mom when she suggested trying a different approach to hunting or for that matter, trapping. They both seemed somewhat deflated after Martha had injected her two cents. Being stupid and ignorant about such matters, I started rattling my mouth, looking for her thoughts which involved both her and I. Uncle Lee suggested I go look at the beaver before dark in an attempt to change the subject, but I abruptly stated that I wanted to hear what Martha had to say regarding the Grey Ghost. Since she was right there, they reluctantly agreed to listen, and Martha just smiled with a knowing expression on her face. She realized her opinion was debatable just like my nose issue. In her calm and graceful refilling of uncle's cup, she affectionately rubbed my uncle's head and just as calmly told both Dad and uncle that they had two weeks to hang that old buck because after their two weeks were up she wanted two weeks to try her luck. Then she told each of them that her two weeks were during Thanksgiving vacation. With a flirtatious swing of her hips, she reminded uncle her two weeks were during the rut. The war was on!

Uncle Lee stood up and challenged Martha by suggesting the loser had to pay for the fox mount and the mount of the Grey Ghost. I was sitting with my mouth open and Dad noticed my wide-eyed stare and chuckled to himself.

Martha started humming her favorite song and danced around confidently. That was the final straw for my uncle, and he reminded her she had learned everything she knew from him and wondered if she had forgotten. She politely informed us that she had learned a few tricks of her own and uncle should have known that. Dad was absolutely mute. My uncle asked if my dad had any objection to this challenge and he agreed reluctantly. "It's okay if my better half agrees," he said.

Martha smiled and confidently replied, "Its okay. I've already cleared it with the boss."

Dad just laughed and said, "You two women have planned this all along. So that's why she bought her license. I thought it was for an extra tag."

Martha giggled and said, "You're getting smarter every day. Your wife has more confidence in Ray's nose than either one of you, so be prepared for the consequences." That's when Dad took the challenge seriously and wisely shut up. Martha laughingly told uncle he could bring in reinforcements if he needed to, such as the codgers. She mentioned she wasn't worried because the codgers were so stuck in their knowledge and the past. I always knew when my uncle felt threatened by his habit of swinging his pocket watch, but along with that habit, he was also scratching his head. This challenge apparently had surprised him, but it was accepted fondly for the moment.

I asked Dad if Mom really hunted and he offered, "Yes she did, before you and your sister were born." He went on to say she had killed her share of rack bucks. Even with that endorsement, I recall thinking there was no chance in hell for Mom and Martha to bag that buck and I wondered how that process involved me. Martha informed us that one of the rules was to stop harassing me regarding my nose and other observations I had made down the Dusty Trail. They both agreed. This whole obsession for the Grey Ghost had the entire family involved except for my sister. I expressed that thought and Martha explained she was also part of our plan. This was crazy, and I remember thinking this could be fun. Trapping was serious business which always was a high priority, yet with this competition there was a serious glitch in everyone's plans at the moment. I couldn't help remembering sister smelling that deer and I was trying to determine where she fit into the plans devised by Martha and Mom.

The discussion around the challenge subsided when Mom and sister appeared out of curiosity and Mom knowingly asked, "What's new?" Sis was oblivious to the events and asked where Freckles was. Everyone laughed and Dad picked her up and hugged her with affection. My sister was dressed in a red snowsuit and sported a red scarf and earmuffs. Uncle Lee laughed and tugged on a pigtail. He always made such a big deal over my sister and oftentimes took her to Blair's Ice Cream Store, which she loved. Martha seemed very happy and handed my sister a cookie, indicating and expressing fondness.

Dad reminded us he had to work days and needed to clean up for bed and indicated I also needed to get ready for bed and prepare for school the following morning. Going back to school hadn't been a thought, but since he mentioned, it I started deflating. My mom wasn't finished and rubbed salt in the wound when she told Dad he needed to come right home after work to baby sit because she and Martha were going to the rifle range to sight in their thirty-thirties. He laughed, but the reality of this challenge was staring him right in the face. That's when my sister pushed my uncle's buttons by saying there's a deer wandering around your back yard. That was when Martha and Mom stood side-by-side and declared, "Let the games begin." My uncle indicated he needed time to check traps in the morning and wanted to put more sets out on different property.

I asked, "Why not put some in the meadow by the pontoon bridge area?" That's when he explained he left several areas free of traps so he could hunt foxes with Freckles without worrying, since that was his first love. I thought about that answer and was thinking I knew that area had as many as five foxes. Fox hunting was fun, but traps seemed easier and they also worked continuously. It took time for me to digest that logic.

My day had been eventful and productive, yet confusing regarding the Grey Ghost, which had triggered some insecurity and reservations. I was fond of Martha and loved Mom, but I had an allegiance to uncle and Dad.

During the walk across the driveway to home, I felt tension and confusion. My mom cleared up my feelings when she referred to the realization that it was time for the two male egos to acknowledge that neither one of them had all the answers. Dad was a bit irritated by her observation and reminded her he believed in my ability to smell deer and she knew it. It was apparent that this standoff was directed primarily toward uncle's lack of recognizing that perhaps it was time to display some humility. Dad responded with, "It's a bit late for that, but you do have a point." I wondered where the line was drawn between loyalty and respect.

The subject was changed to work, school and preparations for bed. My sister was falling asleep in Dad's arms, which always gave everyone a true sense of love and affection. As we walked into the small kitchen area, the warmth felt soothing from the wood fire. The chore of undressing sister was funny because she was sound asleep on her feet. Dad and Mom laughed and directed me to wash and get myself ready for bed. Exhaustion was prevalent, but my family was united with security and safety.

Being awakened for school, my first reaction and thoughts were about the traps, and I looked outside through the window and my uncle was gone and so was Martha's truck. While having breakfast, Mom informed me it was sloppy and dirty since the snow was melting, so boots were necessary. God, I hated those black boots with the buckles that caused so much trouble. While complaining about the boots, Mom's usual answer spilled out. "Be thankful you have boots, because some of your friends aren't so fortunate." That explanation was old and I wished I wasn't so lucky. I hated those boots. My sister had white boots that snapped and seemed easier to deal with.

She had no complaints. Walking toward school to meet our friends, my sister went one way and I headed over to meet Sam and Joe. It was Monday, so heading to school kept the conversation at a minimum. I did tell my buddies about the beaver and fox and there was very little reaction. I looked back to check Sis and she was all right walking along with her friend. Mom was right, the roads were muddy and poor Joe had on sneakers that were totally wet.

Walking up to the classroom, Mrs. Smith was standing at the door telling everyone to put their coats in the cloak room and place boots under our coats. She also informed the class to stand because it was time to seat everyone by their class averages. I was angry with this whole process, since it caused serious anxiety and humiliation except for the smart girls in the class. This was always a problem for my friend who had serious learning difficulties. My first reaction about this stupid exercise was tolerance, but that wasn't going to happen today. I had planned to take a stand before and the time had come. I had learned to accept life on life's terms, but I also knew about fairness and humiliation. This whole process always caused tears and unnecessary animosity.

With everyone standing at attention waiting for the list of doom to be drawn out of her desk I walked to the last seat in the class room and sat down. All of my classmates were shocked and looked over in disbelief. That's when Mrs. Smith looked up and realized my intention. She stood staring with her arms folded and tapped her right foot indicating meanness. Her disposition wasn't friendly, but then again it never was. In a very assertive voice she yelled, "Ray, get on your feet and be prepared for placement." I never moved a muscle. I can recall sweat running down my neck while bracing for serious physical encounter. The atmosphere was tense and my buddies fidgeted with nervousness. She started walking slowly toward me with her ruler tapping her hand with that threat. I was prepared for the confrontation and decided to suffer the consequences. As that miserable teacher kept walking toward me, slapping that ruler on her palm, I prepared myself for a trashing. Just before she got close enough to swing I stood up with my own ruler, which I had placed in my jeans. I slapped my ruler on the desk and told Joe and Sam to get Miss Stone, the principal. They ran out and I heard them yelling and running toward her office. I stood my ground and threatened her by telling her my uncle was a cop and if she tried to hit me with that ruler I was prepared to fight back.

It was then I heard a voice yell, "Edith, get away from Ray and put down that ruler." It was Miss Stone, standing near the door with two other teachers who had heard the commotion. All of my classmates were scared, and for that matter so was I. Mrs. Smith told the principal that I had defied her instruction and I needed disciplining. My principal told my teacher to go to the teacher's lounge and she would be right there.

Mrs. Smith stormed out and pushed Miss Horn as she rushed by. The principal told everyone to sit while she attended to this matter. Not one word was spoken by my classmates and they all sat down quickly. Miss Stone told me to go to her office and she would attend to me later. At that time, I really didn't care what was going to transpire and was more than willing to suffer the consequences.

Walking slowly toward the office, my thoughts were scrambled and I can remember feeling scared, but satisfied. The entire school was buzzing with excitement and even the school janitor was roaming the hall. I always liked Mr. Howard and when he said, "It's about time somebody stood their ground about that bitch," I realized he must have witnessed other situations that involved my teacher.

The secretary in the office was talking on the phone and when I walked in she smiled and told me to sit down. I had never been in this office before and there was a photo of President Eisenhower with a flag standing beside it. The phone rang with several calls that she dismissed because the villain was sitting in front of her.

I recall looking at the clock, which had large roman numerals. Even in this pickle in which I found myself, I wondered how my uncle was faring on the trap line. My insides started churning and I really wanted to cry, but suppressed that need due to my stubbornness that I now knew came from uncle.

About fifteen minutes later, Miss Stone came in and calmly told me that she had called my parents and had informed them about the situation. She said, "Ray, what do you have to say for yourself regarding this difficulty?" I never stuttered, but found myself grasping for words and it was immediately apparent what I needed to say. I looked at Miss Stone and quoted my uncle: "Always treat people with kindness; it always feels good." It seemed appropriate at the time and I instantly knew I had been right standing my ground trying to protect my classmate from any further humiliation.

I heard my mom and dad in the hall talking to Mr. Howard, and that's when Miss Stone got out of her chair to get my parents. I became really anxious and felt fearful, but surprisingly calm. I could overhear the conversation and realized that Mrs. Smith had lied and obviously changed the truth and that's when another quote came to me: "Never get into a pissing match with a skunk."

My parents walked into the office and Miss Stone dismissed her secretary, so privacy was an obvious concern. This whole ordeal was out of character for my parents and they honestly seemed disgusted with my behavior. My mother was tense with some evidence of shock. Dad, on the other hand, seemed a bit calmer except for getting to the truth. He politely informed Miss Stone that regardless of the teacher's account, he wanted my version and the opinion of some of the other students.

The principal was clearly taken aback by his delivery and tried to dismiss his interpretation of what needed to take place. He informed Miss Stone that he was a student of Mrs. Smith in the seventh grade and even in those days, she was brutal regarding her interpretation of motivating students. He went on to say that Mrs. Smith carried a ruler which she often used to assert her authority. The principal sat back, took a deep breath which seemed to indicate that she had been placed in a bad position which she hadn't anticipated. My father continued with two very pertinent questions. "Is it a common practice to place students in order of their grade average and is it necessary in today's world to slap or emotionally insult children at any age? If these practices are being implemented by Mrs. Smith, she's not fit to teach my son or any other student, for that matter. I obviously don't know this for certain, but I imagine her file is full of complaints, so maybe you should re-think how you plan to approach this. I will admit that my son certainly isn't an angel and he has his faults, but he won't lie and he has never shown aggressive behavior before. Based on my observation right now, I believe it's your responsibility to provide evidence that what transpired was Ray's fault."

Dad also asked for a formal hearing with the school superintendent, as well as a cross-section of my classmates which needed to be assembled as soon as possible. Then he dropped the bomb! "When I was in Mrs. Smith's class, I had a confrontation with her regarding slapping my friend Melvin and there was a formal complaint made by my mom and Melvin's parents. Mrs. Smith was reprimanded and given leave for performance issues. She was severely disciplined by her superiors, so from my perspective Ray simply finished what my mother and other parents started. That information is on file somewhere, so I would suggest you start investigating all of the significant facts. That teacher has been a problem in this school for years and you know it, and I expect her dismissal without me even talking to my son."

During this lecture by Dad, my mother sat listening to his presentation of the facts, which I later found out was discussed during the ride over to deal with this conflict. My dad politely informed Miss Stone he was taking me home and would handle the situation regarding my behavior in an appropriate manner. Miss Stone stood and shook both parents' hands and said I would be expected back at school the following day. The only thing that came out of Mom's mouth was that I would be in school only if Mrs. Smith wasn't there and to let her know about the school's final decision. That's when a very important statement was made by Miss Stone, who gave my parents and I complete satisfaction. We were informed that Mrs. Smith had been formally dismissed, pending further investigation by the superintendent and the school board.

Walking out of school with my parents, not one word was spoken and I was filled with mixed emotions ranging from confusion to feelings of satisfaction. It was a terrible experience having such complex issues being discussed and knowing I had taken a serious stance that I later learned was very controversial. In those days, discipline was usually dished out by taking the adult's word over the child's, so I expected some form of serious reprimand, but was surprised to learn on our way home that my actions had created some serious implications that would be dealt with after calming down. My parents seemed upset, yet they appeared more relaxed than angry. I was asked if I had any concerns and if I was prepared for any repercussions that might take place. I slowly responded that I knew of the possibilities, but my sister was still in school and I wondered if she had heard or knew about this situation. Dad stopped the car immediately and turned it around and headed back to school to get my sister. In all the confusion it never entered their thoughts to consider her reaction when she heard about this mess.

When Sis got into the back seat, she laughed and told me I was in serious trouble with Mrs. Smith and that I would probably get a licking. Both parents were shocked by her reaction but ignored her comment for the time being. My sister poked me and smiled behind my parents back making me wonder why sisters always enjoyed their brothers getting into trouble. She seemed pleased and excited to get out of school early at my expense.

Dad pulled the car into the drive, let Mom and us out and obviously headed back to work.

Walking into the house, I felt tired from the tension that was creeping into my thoughts. My mom was very subdued and deep in thought. The phone rang, which my mom answered, and after talking briefly told me to go outside and find something to do. That indicated her call was related to me and she obviously wanted me out of hearing distance. I put my coat and hat on and started looking for my packs, which I found behind the wood stove, drying out.

It was a warm October day and most of the snow had melted so everything seemed wet and dreary. Looking around for some activity, I slowly walked off the porch feeling lost and alone. During moments like these I always knew the one friend I had in the whole world at the time was Freckles. After unleashing him, we headed for our special place ~ the Dusty Trail. Freckles was energetic and wanted to play, but he soon understood I wasn't in the mood. He suddenly stopped running around in circles looking for attention and I saw his enthusiasm dwindle. Freckles always realized or understood my disposition without having to explain.

It seemed as if I always managed to create issues, even when I tried to do something nice or what I perceived as being kind. The issue of standing up for what's right always propagated some unforeseen consequences. Freckles stayed at my side and the two of us wandered aimlessly toward our favorite sanctuary. The leaves were still falling off the trees and I kicked at them as I walked. It was cool and my hands were getting cold, so I slipped them into my school jeans. My red flannel shirt that uncle bought me was warm and comfortable. The chickadees were feeding and chirping, which always stimulated comfort and I forced a smile and grin. The emotional turmoil was slowly diminishing, even though I seemed to enjoy this time to wallow in self-pity. Energy was slowly seeping into my body and I started to run toward the trail as fast as my skinny legs would take me. My best friend relished in this burst and my problems started to dissipate. The two of us frolicked together running, skipping and jogging in a graceful, carefree manner.

Breaking a branch off a small maple tree, I stripped off the bark and smelled the clean, bark-free stick because I loved that smell. That habit still comforts me today. After reaching the apple tree that was my destination, I looked around, wondering what my uncle remembered about this small orchard that had been abandoned, just like the old farm. I noticed a few apples hanging on a branch that I couldn't reach, so I looked for a long branch on the ground to knock them off. Accomplishing that effort, I bit into the sweetest apple I ever had. I filled my pockets with four or five apples and I remember wishing Freckles could enjoy one. His diet was primarily dog food, some table scraps and occasionally some leftover venison.

Sitting down with my friend and putting my arm around his neck for comfort, life seemed more complicated every day. I remember visualizing Mrs. Smith tapping her right foot and hitting her palm with that ruler and I chuckled internally, recalling the look on her homely face when I stood my ground. That old miserable lady seemed so very unhappy I actually felt sorry for her.

The heat from Freckles' body was welcoming, but he jumped up and started running up the path for no apparent reason. Getting up slowly to investigate, I saw Uncle Lee walking slowly towards me with a concerned smile on his face. As he got closer, I started to run toward him and he knelt down and put his arms out for me and I ran into them for comfort. He hugged me with such love and security I started to cry harder than I had ever cried before. He kept saying, "It's okay, Ray, get it out. It needs to get out, so cry and just remember I'm here." Freckles was sitting next to us and my uncle and I put our arms around him and the three of us were united in love, safety and best of all, comfort. He held me for several minutes and calmly raised his aging body gradually and he put his two rugged, wrinkled hands on my cheeks and wiped the tears away with his thumbs.

The smell of Yankee Girl was so soothing that my heart and soul went into his arms again for a hug of reassurance. That old rustic uncle loved me and my God, at that moment I certainly loved and relished his love and concern. Freckles realized the significance of this display of emotion and whined softly. There are very few moments in life that revitalize and validate honest displays of love coupled with respect and concern. Words were never uttered as the two of us walked together hand-in-hand while Freckles followed and we walked slowly toward home. There was no reason for verbal communication because my uncle realized I needed time to regain my composure void of reliving the traumatic events that had transpired at school. With our hands clasped together, the magic of his presence allowed me to slowly recover internally, allowing myself the luxury of returning back to the safety of my family, both emotionally and physically. Words wouldn't have helped, but the calm and peace that flowed between our hands started to renew my faith in the human spirit.

I recall his slow, graceful walk along the Dusty Trail and wondered how often he had wandered down this trail with his hounds looking for answers to life's problems, so he probably knew immediately where I had gone seeking peace and understanding.

Just before reaching the cutoff to our homes, he slowly guided me in a direction that I hadn't taken in some time. I never questioned his motive, but just wallowed in his comfort. Finally he broke his silence by explaining he wanted to show me something which might help ease my confusion and disillusionment about human problems. I was open for anything that made sense in dealing with emotional turmoil. I recall thinking I knew why he had quit school to live and enjoy the peace and tranquility that nature had to offer. My uncle pointed toward a huge, old oak tree I was familiar with and the three of us walked slowly in that direction. I was amazed when he softly told me to watch my step because there was a root he always caught his toe in and it had tripped him more than once. That old tree and this rustic old man had obviously been friends for years long before I had been born. I asked how long it had been since he had been back there and he replied at least fifteen years. He offered, "It's grown up some, but that old oak still overlooks every thing around its home." I asked how old that tree would be and he answered,

"It was huge and old when I was your age, so only the maker knows for sure." That made perfect sense, even to me, and it filled me with wonder and some understanding regarding nature and how this tree survived in spite of the odds. He knew I understood and seemed to relish the fact that no further explanation was needed. Getting closer to the oak and the ridge that was located just fifty yards below, its base the purpose for this detour, was suddenly prevalent in my thoughts.

Reaching the base of this old oak, my uncle looked around at the ground and paced off six long paces, and then he stopped and started kicking leaves and dirt about three inches deep. With some relief and happiness on his face, he asked me to help him kick away the dirt and leaves. While helping uncle, I was shocked to find a flat stone approximately four feet square. He took his gloves and started brushing off the remaining dirt and leaves. I helped, and soon the explanation for this effort appeared and I sat down in amazement. My uncle continued cleaning and even used his old sweatshirt to help give me a better look. There were thirteen names engraved in this stone, ranging from my grandmother and grandfather to all the names of my uncles and aunts in the order they were born, with just one exception. Between my dad's name and his younger sister was the name *Raymond*. Reaching down he wiped that name cleaner and started explaining about his nephew who passed away at the age of three from a deadly flu virus and he had asked my Dad and Mom to name me Raymond in honor of that child, and they had agreed with his suggestion. Then he wiped off another area and I could see that he had chiseled the image of several doves flying toward this old oak tree.

Leaning his body against the trunk of the old oak I felt a bit insignificant in comparison to the tree that was holding up my old rustic uncle. Both had years of experience, yet they still managed to survive in spite of the tears and fears that encompass the entire living experience. They represented longevity, strength and other virtues acquired over decades of trials and tribulations that obviously no one can avoid if you're true to yourself, even when you make poor decisions for all the right reasons.

My uncle slowly and graphically described how and why he had taken the time and energy to chisel the family names and dates into this strategically located flat stone. "Ray, let me try to describe the meaning of this effort," he said. "During the years after your grandfather passed, I assumed the responsibility of trying to raise your aunts and uncles. They were all smart, energetic and basically fair and honest children. Like all children, they needed support and at times, discipline. I was honored and grateful for the opportunity to become a surrogate dad to these kids and the rewards I received back cannot be expressed. In fact, they are too numerous to mention. Every one of those names engraved represents a person who possessed a unique personality and character that needed to be nurtured and developed. My God, Ray, some days were so full of emotion I often wondered how your grandmother and I managed to recognize who needed the most attention. This wasn't always easy, and I came to realize failure would be part of the equation. Failure is painful and always leaves a lasting impression. The entire process demanded energy coupled with love, regardless of circumstances. When the time came for each of them to leave the nest and fly into life on their own, I always felt empty and sad as they spread their wings because I knew life could be painful and unfair. There are no guarantees, so it's necessary to accept life on life's terms. To be frank and honest, that's just the way life is. Your namesake, Raymond, was a smart and vibrant boy who required and demanded attention from his older brothers and sisters. He was determined to please, but he also caused some turmoil on occasion. He walked at nine months and started talking very early because his older siblings played and interacted with him constantly. When he became ill and passed, my entire emotional stability was challenged. My sister felt responsible, which was normal, yet she never really completely recovered from his passing."

"Ray, I'm sure you must be wondering how this relates to the problems that surfaced today at school, so let me try and explain the best way I know how. First of all, the entire situation was created by a very old and miserable teacher who apparently had been disillusioned with her life and took her anger out in the classroom. I personally knew Mrs. Smith and for that matter, so does Martha. That poor lady has always lived a life filled with anger and self-inflicted loneliness. She created problems everywhere she taught, but somehow managed to hold onto her job in spite of problems she created. Your decision to stand up for your friend is similar to my relationship with Walking Charlie, so I understand and have empathy for your desire to protect your friend. I know you learned today that there are consequences that surface when a decision is made that contradicts the establishment. Make no mistake; your teacher is part of that establishment. It took tremendous courage to stand up for the beliefs that came from your upbringing. Lessons such as this will continue throughout your life, but honesty and purpose always bring satisfaction that is the result of trying to do the right thing. It's never easy when confronting poor behavior. Always remember the risk involved. When making difficult decisions, you take a stand based on what's right. Your dilemma, from my perspective, is wholesome and it originated from values that you've been taught. To stand your ground at your age is rare; but I'm not surprised. I believe that your namesake guided you and understood it was time to correct that wrong. I want you to always remember this event even after I'm gone. I want you to pick your battles based on what your parents have taught you regarding caring and sharing no matter who says otherwise. You'll always know what's right by the feeling deep in your soul. I have always known right from wrong based on that premise."

"I ask you to keep this tribute to your family a secret until you're older, but never forget that your Uncle Raymond is always with you and I expect consistency in your life pursuits. You'll know when you cross the line by simply feeling guilty or uneasy. Ray, having watched and observed your basic personality, it is apparent that throughout your future life you'll always be tempted to go down the path less traveled. That characteristic is similar to mine, but be aware trouble will occasionally raise its ugly head due to the fact that most people will usually take the easier and much softer path. That's all right, but your tendency to challenge and question traditional behavior will tend to threaten certain individuals. Just be aware of that reality. If nothing else about this day stays with you, try to remember decisions are usually right if they feel good deep down in your soul. No one is always right, so be prepared to admit your faults and mistakes. Also, make honest attempts to make certain you do not make the same mistakes over and over. Your future will always be more positive than negative if you practice these principals in your decision making."

Reaching out, I gladly took his wrinkled and calloused hand in mine. Looking up at his face, it was perhaps the first time I really understood the meaning of a spiritual encounter.

I'm amazed thinking back over that conversation how my uncle could have know that I would be capable of digesting and comprehending his entire presentation that covered the day's events. He knew I was always going to remember that experience. Nothing more could be said, so we started to walk back.

Halfway home, my uncle laughed and with a bit of a hop he informed me I had caught another nice red which needed skinning. Happiness surfaced once again when he offered his congratulations, stating "Ray, you sure as hell earned your keep today," and we both laughed with love and honest understanding that the three of us were taking the same path which made it possible to experience success and failure with acceptance.

Getting close to the back of the trapper's shed, my uncle told me he had called Martha and explained the situation at school. He told me to expect her to show up for supper to help explain the process necessary to rectify the decisions my parents would make in having to deal with Mrs. Smith and the school system. He informed me not to change my stance and simply hold true to the truth and everything would be all right.

Walking toward the trapper's shed to skin the fox and two beavers, my dad appeared wearing his old jeans and shirt. He informed us he had already finished skinning and the pelts were stretched and drying. He reached out his arms and gave me a hug, indicating everything was all right in his eyes. Three generations were obviously walking down the same path which helped to end the painful chapter regarding Mrs. Smith and the sad consequences of her unfortunate poor behavior.

CHAPTER 18

Consequences of My Actions

Sadly, the entire process painfully diminished a teaching career that spanned forty years. It saddens me today knowing I helped destroy a reputation with one brave display of standing up for basic fundamental values I felt needed protecting. I had learned that poor ethics and selfish purpose eventually comes back to haunt people with poor values when constantly displayed over time. I also became aware and learned from uncle's observations and his explanation of the facts that standing firmly for honest and fair convictions usually results in fairness and justice if based on the truth. The fact that Mrs. Smith arrogantly never learned from her past mistakes eventually perpetuated her demise which, unfortunately, she deserved. At my age, I certainly wasn't capable of digesting the entire process that encapsulated that debate, yet it felt right, regardless of causing all the confusion my stance caused the entire adult establishment.

That evening, sitting around the supper table with the company of uncle and Martha, the complex stance I had taken was the topic of conversation since the entire school community had been obviously turned upside-down. The entire teaching profession was threatened, which hadn't been challenged very often by a student my age during those years. Let there be no mistake that all the controversy was more complicated than I had anticipated. I didn't get off scot-free for my stance. I received one very significant lecture about the actual confrontation. My parents were very upset and disappointed with the fact that I had used my ruler as a weapon. That one issue caused concern. Therefore, I was chastised and received a modest disciplinary action due to my display of aggression. The penalty I received wasn't severe. I was expected to thoroughly clean the doghouses, which was always my job to begin with. The only difficulty that I encountered was the cold, damp weather this job was executed in.

It was during supper that evening when the subject of the Grey Ghost raised its head, giving me the opportunity to verbalize my concern and discomfort with being forced to switch my allegiance from uncle and Dad over to Mom and Martha. Once again, it was obvious I hadn't learned completely how adults tend to complicate even a small insignificant statement. It surprisingly generated a bit of controversy. I awkwardly tried to explain that I felt torn because I inadvertently once again changed and challenged their own perceptions of their future plans for bagging the Grey Ghost. I recall feeling emotionally torn between my love and commitment to everyone concerned. It was emotionally and physically exhausting and I looked forward to going to bed and I badly needed some sleep. I honestly wanted to avoid any further discussions that had anything to do with the events of this extremely difficult day. I recall thinking that life always seemed less complicated when Freckles and I were left alone without so many performance issues. Adults sure could complicate simplicity in life.

Supper that evening consisted of rabbit hindquarters slowly simmered in tomato sauce and served over noodles. The vegetables were mixed green and yellow wax beans with a few carrots mixed in for color. The traditional and usual homemade bread was served warm. The butter melted easily, just the way I liked it. These simple, yet tasty meals always seemed to comfort everyone, which usually improved their disposition. The details of my problem went back and forth. The discussion about the possibilities for the school's position with speculation about reaching a simple compromise was battered about. Not knowing much about all the technical jargon, my blank stare was noticed by uncle. Taking his butter knife in his right hand and using it as a pointer, he slowly stood and he looked a bit annoyed. Walking toward my sister and reaching his empty hand toward hers, he told everyone that my courage, insight, and strong conviction would make school easier and less stressful for all the students that might have had to tolerate Mrs. Smith's bull crap ever again. He continued with, "In my opinion, there is no room for negotiation based on that reality. I feel strongly that Ray's effort was based on the strong beliefs that we have instilled in him. It's no time to force a compromise of his honest effort. Reaching a happy ending for the sake of making life easier for the guilty parties shouldn't diminish his integrity and compassion for his friend. Do what you feel is right, since he's your son, but you might want to think about destroying the faith we have all engrained in his honest and brave attempt to bring justice into the school system. I'm sorry, but that's just my feeling. In my opinion, there should be no room for negotiation in this matter. He stood up for his friends, his sister and all of Mrs. Smith's past and future students. This matter is over and a serious wrong has been corrected."

Martha tried to inject some alternative, but for the second time in my observations of uncle, he slowly raised his free hand, indicating the end of conversation. Then he simply asked me to accompany him to the trapper's shed.

My sister asked if she could go too, so uncle reached down and lifted her lovingly in his arms saying, "Yes, Cindy, you're also ready for your entry into a better understanding regarding everything you're witnessing," and she hugged uncle and he gently kissed her cheek. I always knew uncle loved Sis and after that gesture no one ever discussed this situation in terms of compromise in my presence again.

Holding my sister in his arm, she nestled her head into his bony shoulder and neck. Turning on a light, we slowly walked into the shed. It was evident that our trip was simply to get away from the intensity of complicated issues. Sitting my sister into the tan recliner, uncle muttered, "Christ, every time too many people get involved they start injecting speculation, which always confuses the primary premise of the problem at hand. Ray, you're learning that living in a system complicated by perceived smart and educated adults usually complicates resolution and results in avoiding the major premise in comprehending the simple logic that resolves most conflict. Adults will beat a dead horse to death! Your dad, mom and even Martha seem bent on speculating exaggerated issues that don't even exist. Try to understand that it's human nature and it's often stupid and ridiculous to debate what is clearly a black-and-white issue. Damn, I spent years asking one simple question: What's the honest and right thing to do? I struggle with bull crap disguised as the truth. This is well over your head, I know, but confusion and ignorance always complicates decision making."

Frankly, it took years to digest his feelings that evening, but over the years I recalled his core value system and it always served me well.

Sis seemed transfixed by uncle and all the fur hanging on the boards drying. She was evidently at peace and felt safe in the comfort of uncle. Those vibes always radiated and flowed easily from his simple, yet profound grasp of reality.

Picking my sister up and holding her with affection, she wallowed in the warmth his personality always possessed.

We walked slowly toward our homes, ready for bed and well-deserved rest. Facing going to school in the morning generated anxiety and reservation until uncle graciously offered to accompany me and Sis to school in the morning if it was approved by our parents. That simple gesture calmed my discomfort and any reservations I had about having to face the issues and problems I had created. I knew sleep would come easily knowing the security, safety and calmness would accompany me at school in the morning. Sis just loved his soothing presence because his grasp of simplicity radiated from every facet of his being.

CHAPTER 19

Returning Back to Normal

Sis and I prepared for bed while our parents cleaned and straightened up the kitchen. Poor Sis was perplexed about the tension displayed that evening. She wandered toward me and asked if I had ever seen uncle so upset. I shook my head no and whispered, "Let Mom and Dad deal with uncle's feelings," since I was firmly on uncle's side.

My sister was so cute when she whispered back, "You're always on his side." The two of us hurried upstairs. She slipped and fell on the landing. Cindy always tried to get ahead of me, which often caused her unnecessary bumps and bruises. That her affection for life was so natural her helped our relationship. In fact, that particular aspect of her personality never ceased to amaze me. After all the formalities for bedtime preparation were completed, Sis and I said good night. The last thing I remember that evening was Cindy offering her feelings about uncle. "Ray, she again whispered, Uncle Lee always helps when we need him."

The following morning, the atmosphere at breakfast was tense, to say the least. Mom was alone since Dad was at work. She looked tired, yet tried to present an air of normalcy. It wasn't working very well if you ask me, so breakfast was fast and furious. Uncle pulled the Nash into the drive and got out leaving the car running to warm it up. He appeared in the kitchen clean shaven with lingering aftershave. He had prepared himself carefully with actual dress pants, shirt and shoes. He was also wearing his dress hat and my mother remarked how handsome he looked and he informed her he could clean up well enough to fool some of the people some of the time. They both laughed and mom thanked him for offering his help getting Cindy and I off to school. "Ethel, he explained, sometimes I feel too strongly about fairness, but occasionally I tend to go overboard." She just nodded with grace, indicating her acknowledgement.

Getting into the back seat, Sis and I were tense for obvious and significant reasons. While driving toward school, my reluctance was apparent and Sis, as usual, offered her opinion, which provided some relief. She just said that it was kind of fun feeling important with a driver all cleaned up. I remember how hard uncle laughed and reminded her not to get accustomed to this treatment.

As we walked hand-in-hand together down the hall toward the office, all of our friends were staring out of curiosity. We were met by Miss Stone, who graciously acknowledged our presence. She put out her hand toward uncle and he removed his hat and shook her hand formally. His presence obviously had her transfixed, indicating all matters had been resolved and really didn't need anymore explaining at the time. Truthfully, she appeared somewhat intrigued with his good looks and calm assertiveness.

Surprisingly, my sister walked toward her classroom alone, which left me to join my classmates who were taking turns peeking down the hall. Miss Stone implied that I should get to class before the bell rang. I slowly turned toward uncle who gestured for me to leave so I did. Walking slowly toward class I noticed a pretty young lady coming towards me and she greeted me warmly. She kindly explained that she was my new teacher and that I could sit anywhere available. That simple gesture allowed me confidence, so walking into class I was greeted fondly by all my classmates, which made all the pain and fear leave my body. Life resumed to a new normal at school. I smiled when it became evident that the friend that I protected was seated in my old seat, so I took the seat she had symbolically vacated and somehow that gesture felt appropriate.

With the school day finished, my friends all injected their thoughts as we walked toward Sam's store. Arsen offered to buy me some baseball cards and I told him to buy Sam a few, which he did. By this display of kindness, my controversial behavior had inadvertently validated standing up for principal and fairness, and it felt good! Freckles met me at the sumac stand which told me uncle was home, since mom never released any hounds. Each and every day had been full of such a drastic pendulum of emotions that Freckles' presence calmed my entire personality.

The weather was cool, with a brisk wind from the west, indicating colder weather would be imminent with possible snow. The entire family dreaded winter, but in Freckles' playful display I quickly dismissed that thought. Upon reaching the steps and porch we were greeted by Mom, who was filled with questions about my new teacher and also questioned the entire day's events. I had expected that interrogation and reluctantly answered in concise, distinct and complete answers that I felt would satisfy her concerns. Uncle was certainly right about adults beating a dead horse.

I asked her if my sister was upstairs or down the street at Linda's and was taken aback when informed she was in the shed with uncle. Leaving the house after changing into old jeans and a shirt, I ran toward the warmth and comfort of that smelly old shed. Walking around the Nash, the trunk had been left opened, so I looked inside. There were some muskrats and two mink that needed skinning. I ran into the shed and stopped dead in my tracks. My five-year-old sister was actually helping uncle finish skinning another large beaver. He looked up over her head and started laughing, realizing how surprised I looked witnessing that weird, but significant event. My sister was wearing jeans with a red flannel shirt under an old bright green sweater, and she was also holding a fleshing tool in work gloves with the fingers hanging around her wrist. Her braids were crooked since uncle had tied a red handkerchief around her nose to help eliminate the odor. Sis looked like a bandit dressed up for Halloween. She was so intense as she was trying to accomplish her task and she seemed oblivious to my presence. I laughed uncontrollably, which snapped her out of the trance. When she noticed me she also started laughing, and all three of us were hysterical with laughter when my mother walked in looking for Sis. Mom's chin dropped to the floor and she put her hand over her mouth. With a bellow of laughter she told uncle she needed a photo to document this event.

After pictures, mom took Cindy in her Halloween costume to clean her up before supper. Laughing as they walked toward home, the feelings being displayed between the four of us seemed to indicate how the entire family adapted so easily to situations that surrounded this simple, but rewarding lifestyle. Nature and wildlife activities were performed naturally and my aging uncle was the glue that helped keep the entire family involved.

While uncle and I finished preparing the mink and muskrats for drying, our conversation was geared mainly about Sis and her desire to participate, which symbolized the family's identity.

With all the fur hanging and drying, the effort and love displayed by my uncle that day at school and with Cindy helping in the shed manifested the basic truths that our lives were simply based on values displayed openly and unconditionally.

The trapping experience wasn't based on money. The entire objective was about where this tradition took everyone, both physically and emotionally. I noticed the table was set for six again, indicating company was expected and they were walking onto the porch. My father welcomed Martha and uncle and he immediately started describing Cindy's effort in the shed. Martha laughed and said, "She's another chip off the old block."

While supper was being served, everyone openly discussed the trauma of the past two days. The topic was changed after laughter put that issue to bed and in its final resting place.

With all of us enjoying fried brook trout and mashed potatoes, complemented with fried venison in mushroom gravy, Martha asked if she could speak. The way she asked to be heard stopped all conversation. With sincerity in her voice, she graciously apologized for not understanding and appreciating how significant our family cohesiveness had been mistakenly underestimated, which forced a change in plans, making it uncomfortable. Her callousness required everyone to adjust by two acts of her insensitive actions. The first situation she mentioned referred to her confusing the attempt to outsmart the Grey Ghost. She simply offered that it would serve our family traditions well if all participated in the hunts without any foolish competition. She simply explained that her interference was inappropriate. She went on to admit that injecting her opinion wasn't very sensitive or perceptive, considering how extremely enthusiastic and emotional every member of the family felt about that conquest. Martha also admitted she had been very intrusive and bold expecting our family to possibly accept a compromise with the higher powers of the school.

She went on to explain further. "Please understand I was an only child," she said. "Family was important; however, extended family values only included a few aunts, uncles and cousins which I barely knew, so my sense of family loyalty was rarely an issue. This entire family has always exhibited closeness and respect for each other which came through hard work, heartache and love. Living alone, I want you to know that my teaching career was rewarding and educational, yet your living experiences are much more valuable and rewarding since you all live somewhat tied to family traditions based on love and fellowship. I'm so very sorry for not recognizing those factors."

With a knowing expression on uncle's face, he removed his glasses and licked his lips while his chin quivered, indicating that his heart had been genuinely touched by her admission and apology. He must have felt a very personal attachment and wanted to accept her awareness and apology. He knew how difficult it was for Martha to apologize.

It was the first time my uncle seemed to lack words, which were escaping him at that moment. Standing up slowly, he appeared deep in thought and I knew that Martha's admission was an indication of her need to feel loved and accepted, not only by my uncle but his entire family, as well. Perhaps that was the first time he completely understood his role as the head of this grateful family. He raised each individual child with love, coupled with the power of example. It was apparent how sensitive this moment was when neither parent spoke nor moved. Sis sat still, waiting for some verbal reaction from Uncle Lee. He never seemed lost for words; however; I feel he was recalling years of memories which were probably spinning deep down in his heart. Taking a deep breath and hitching his pants, he slowly reached for my dad's hand. Taking it gently, my father understood his vulnerability, so he stood and hugged uncle and they both supported each other in that display of affection and respect that had been earned through patience, tolerance, consistency and love. My mom's eyes was filled with tears with this depth of love rarely displayed openly between my uncle and my father. Then uncle took his gold pocket watch out from his dress pants and unhooked it from the thin gold chain. Surprising Dad, he caringly handed it to him. On the back of that watch, which had been gifted to my uncle by his sister, who was my dad's mother, were these sensitive words: "To my loving brother and my son you choose after I'm gone." Under that message was inscribed, "From your thankful sister Edith and Mom."

"That old well-worn watch is now in my son's pocket," said uncle, "ready to be distributed once again when appropriate to a family member of my son's choice."

Fortunately, my sister injected her need for some blackberry pie and ice cream. Thank God for my sister. Cindy always displayed poor timing. However, this simple break in emotions was clearly welcomed by the adults.

Eating our pie and ice cream, the mood was quite somber, yet the feeling of contentment radiated.

With the dishes being washed by the ladies, the trappers sat in the living room, engrossed in ideas and thoughts on tactics that needed developing if my nose theory was to be utilized. Sitting next to uncle, I listened intently while he described the Grey Ghost's patterns of behavior which he had displayed in past years. With a pencil and paper on the coffee table, he sketched the shape of the swamp with boulders and other distinctive markers. My uncle had surveyed that swamp and drew a map in such detail it made me wonder if he had lived there himself. His entire concentration was flowing into that map. Wind directions were included, along with runways other deer used, but not the Ghost. The Ghost was similar to uncle and myself because he also took the path least traveled. When he started sketching the corn fields and meadows he stopped and looked at Dad. He asked him if he remembered missing that trophy on November thirteenth the previous year at three o'clock during a blinding snowstorm.

"Yes," was Dad's answer. They were both transfixed by memories and seemed absorbed with past hunts with a focus on the future. My father stood up and started pacing, a habit I inherited that indicated an idea was being mulled over in his head. Both men had very similar body language, which I also display. When dad picked up the pencil, uncle sat back ready to listen. The entire dialogue that flowed between those two was so smooth that even today my memory recalls every word and gesture that was being vocalized and displayed. Before dad started expounding his theory, he walked in my direction, indicating a question heading my way. Thinking back over that evening, the intensity was strong and was building so high that I started feeling like I felt just before a spelling test. Uncle was serious while my father articulated his ideas when he suddenly stopped, knelt down and asked one simple question. "Ray, I need to know one very important detail that you and you alone can answer. Do you have any idea how far off you can smell a buck?" This certainly wasn't any time for speculation and generalities. This question was asked with a need for a specific answer. He realized the pressure and rephrased the question. "Try to explain to uncle how far you start smelling bucks down the Dusty Trail while you are sitting in the apple tree and approximately how far off is that buck before you actually see him? For example, think of the oak out front as the apple tree and think would it be close to the distance to the street corner or another street marker?" I thought for what felt like several minutes when it occurred to me that my ability to describe distances was not probably accurate; however, I could show them exactly what I had experienced firsthand. I told them that the corner was close but I wouldn't swear to it. Both were elated with that answer so the back-and-forth started again.

That old buck wasn't predictable in his movements, which complicated dad's idea. After sitting and holding my desire to speak, an opportunity presented itself. It had been mentioned many times how the Grey Ghost circled around hunters avoiding detection, which sparked an idea I felt might help. To my surprise, they actually sat and listened. "I think you can use his capability to your benefit. His strength may also be his weakness." Uncle sat up briskly and then stood with obvious understanding and excitement. Uncle wondered where I had learned about strengths and weaknesses in regards to changing one for the other. I informed them that I had heard Whitey Ford explain that idea while pitching against the Dodgers.

He laughed and replied "Christ, Leon, he can't spell, but he may be the next Yankee manager after Stengel." My father rustled my hair which always indicated love. The women were hard at work playing a card game called Old Maid that Martha expressed suited her just fine. That joke went over my head, but the adults laughed.

Watching my sister, she always tried to cheat; however, in Martha's presence she appeared to be on good behavior before she got caught cheating. She might have fooled the two ladies, but certainly not me.

Mom asked if we had killed the Grey Ghost with a cute smirk on her face. My mother had always displayed a dry, but appropriate sense of humor.

CHAPTER 20

The Loss of a Good Friend

At home that evening, our conversations covered everyone's interests. A sense of normality was regained which hadn't been apparent during the past several days. Our routine was slowly reclaiming a much needed respite from all the drama.

The next morning, I wasn't filled with the dreadful feeling that usually indicated my reluctance to head back to school. In fact, I was pleased to find out that the experience wasn't half bad with our new teacher. There was some actual enjoyment displayed, not only by me, but also my buddies. The simple process that accompanied daily living seemed so much easier to accept since school wasn't so stressful anymore. As school was dismissed at three-thirty, our normal routine of heading toward Sam's store was no longer part of the plan because baseball cards had somehow lost their mystique. Most of the conversation with my friends had changed to the topic of hockey, with arguments over the Red Wings, Bruins and the Canadians. The major debate was over Gordie Howe of the Red Wings versus Rocket Richard of the Canadians. That discussion never went anywhere because my friend Joey always started interjecting statistics that invariably complicated the entire discussion.

Dropping off my books with homework assignments tucked away safely inside my note book, I ran toward the shed for my daily injection of reality. The Nash was there, but uncle was missing and the garage was locked. I walked toward the back door of uncle's home, which was always open. Walking inside, I noticed the lights were off. This seemed strange. It was very dreary and so much colder than normal. I noticed that the fire had gone out in the wood stove. I yelled for uncle and there was no response. Then I heard him walking around slowly upstairs. I yelled to get his attention. He acknowledged my presence, but offered nothing more. I walked to the stairs and asked if he was all right. He answered with, "Be right down." I was filled with confusion and fear because I sensed that the mood was somber with very weird vibes present in this old kitchen. I returned to the stove, which still had some evidence of hot coals, making an attempt to put a few pieces of wood in. Then I heard uncle start to slowly descend the stairs. I turned on the kitchen light and closed the door to the wood stove after seeing the logs catch fire. The house was very cold and extremely damp. Turning around, I was shocked to witness my uncle standing there holding his red plaid hunting pants in his hands and only wearing his one piece red flannel underwear. He looked tired, worn and very sad. He seemed preoccupied and distant. That vision of my uncle's appearance evoked feelings which made me aware of his age and health. I tried my best to ignore the obvious.

My uncle sat in an old rocking chair and slowly pulled on his pants, indicating he was tired, yet determined. His hair was messy and fell onto his face and over his eyes. Slipping on his packs with noticeable effort he asked how my day at school had gone. He didn't wait for my response. He simply started making some coffee which he obviously needed. This scene was so surreal and it made me painstakingly aware of his frail physical and emotional state. I was transfixed on the tension and reality that this old, vulnerable man was displaying.

He struggled as he performed a simple task which I saw him handle effortlessly numerous times before. I sheepishly asked if he was okay but there was no response. I should have been scared, but my concern geared toward my uncle's well-being was more of a concern in my mind.

After making coffee and taking a seat at the table, I noticed his eyes showed weariness without the normal sparkle. To deny the reality of his vulnerable state which encircled this difficult, but honest experience, it was evident in the personality of this sensitive old man that he was in serious emotional pain. With the coffee pot perking and the stove putting off heat, he asked me to sit down so we could talk. I obeyed as usual; however, it was more out of concern and respect than need. I was a bit hyper with feelings flowing that were new to me. He reached out his hand for mine. I was acutely aware it was for his own personal comfort, indicating that for the very first time our roles had reversed. Sipping his black coffee, he struggled as he tried to hold back tears. His chin quivered trying to hold back emotion. Then, he finally spoke and told me very quietly that our good friend Mutt had passed away that afternoon.

My God, nothing could have prepared me for that information. My uncle squeezed my hand while tears flowed. His frail body shook from shock or disbelief. I was surprised at my own personal strength. I somehow realized if I lost control it would worsen his attempt to regain his grasp on the reality of dealing with his internal feelings that were compromised at the time. We just sat with no need to move from our place, side-by-side, sharing his grief of having lost his friend of over sixty-five years. I was choked up with tears more for my uncle than Mutt, which may have been selfish, I realize, but the attempt to comfort my uncle was the primary objective for the moment. Uncle got up for more coffee and asked if I wanted

154

Ray Hazel

a cup, so I said yes. That was another first in our relationship.
He slowly poured the coffee for us, which he badly needed.
As I sipped mine, I was suddenly aware that the taste of coffee must be something one had to acquire over time. I realized
it was time to ask a few simple questions regarding Mutt's
death. My uncle took a very deep breath and reluctantly started explaining some details that had transpired that afternoon.

That morning, my uncle finished checking sets which had
produced two foxes and several rats on Clayton's property. He
also had two beaver that had been targeted on Mr. Helmer's
pond. The morning was cold and cloudy, which typified early
November. After having coffee at the Silver Grill, uncle decided to ride around Mutt's line looking for the companionship
of his friend. After finding evidence of Mutt's truck tracks,
my uncle had driven down an old logging road that Mutt and
uncle liked to hunt. Mutt enjoyed that area for its graphic
scenery and the area had always produced fur for him. Getting
out of the old Nash, uncle had walked toward the beaver pond
where Mutt had parked his old truck. The truck was still running, which surprised my uncle. When uncle walked alongside the truck, he saw Mutt's arm hanging out of the window
and Mutt was slouched over the steering wheel. Uncle said he
made every attempt to revive Mutt, but it was fruitless. The
entire description was considerably graphic, but I understood
uncle's need to vent. After getting help and calling the appropriate family members, my uncle drove around breaking the
news to the codgers and other significant friends and relatives.
My broken uncle suddenly seemed angry and mad. There was
evidence in the driveway that company had arrived so I got
up to investigate. Weasel, Leo and Simple Simon were slowly
walking toward the back door. They all looked as if they had
been beaten to within an inch of their lives. The entire mood
was filled with sadness with a profound reality that there were

only four codgers left who all displayed pain, and from an emotional standpoint they appeared lost.

The codgers walked into the kitchen saying absolutely nothing. My uncle sat there staring out the window that overlooked the hounds. Leo finally broke the tension by saying, "Our teams need a catcher and goalie. Where in the hell will we find another so tough or tenacious?" My uncle stood and looked everyone in the eyes then replied that Mutt had asked the Lord for a fastball, but the Lord had thrown him a curve that Mutt just couldn't handle. They all nodded in agreement. It was evident that my presence was hindering their ability to openly discuss their feelings filled with tragedy and grief. I simply put two more logs on the fire and started out the kitchen door.

Then Simon said, "Ray, your friend Mutt gave me these the other day to give to you." Simon threw a small bag in my direction which I caught with grace and confidence.

Weasel smiled and said, "I guess he's the natural substitute catcher." The small bag was filled with butterscotch candies. When everyone realized the significance of that gesture, the mood elevated slightly. I excused myself after tucking the bag into my jeans. I reluctantly stepped outside into the cold dreary weather that symbolized the early evening's atmosphere.

I walked slowly toward Freckles instinctively. He must have sensed my emotions, because he just there sat looking at me through his one eye. The other old redbone hound also made his way toward me, and I felt that symbolized understanding. That old hound was also struggling and I wondered if he was also recalling memories of his youth. At one time he had been at the top of his game, but age had relegated him to the sidelines. I ran toward the front porch and yelled to my mom. When she opened the door I noticed a concerned look on her face, indicating the news had deeply touched her. She very kindly asked how I was feeling, which indicated she had known all along where I had been the past hour. I asked permission to go for a walk and she okayed the request. She only asked that I be back before dark. I nodded and left for the comfort of my hounds.

I unhooked Freckles with a feeling of peace and warmth. I looked over at the old redbone who sat alone looking lost and extremely sad, like the mood that death of a friend creates. I unleashed him also and with my two hounds at my side, I walked toward the Dusty Trail, not really understanding why that trail always drew me for comfort. I noticed that old hound limp from battle scars of the past and his vibrant youth. That old redbone kept plugging along without complaint. Freckles never wandered too far off without looking back and as usual, waited for his old, tired friend. Watching that behavior helped me digest some questions I had never been seriously confronted with in my short, yet significant life.

I started to gain some awareness regarding some simple truths that I had fortunately learned in Sunday school. For the first time I was acutely living the reality and truth these lessons which were directly helping explain the complex feelings that death was always painfully confusing, regardless of age. Reaching the meadow near the old orchard, both hounds let out a bellow only hounds can produce. It symbolized a tribute to Mutt and the codgers who all had hunted with that old loyal redbone who had taught the inexperienced younger dogs some tricks of their trade. That old hound sat looking around and appeared calm and relaxed. He also appeared to be engrossed with a peaceful recollection of past hunts with Mutt and his loving, loyal friends who were all reliving those memories. I started feeling much better and reached into my pocket for a butterscotch candy. It tasted wonderful and

I looked up into heaven and simply said, "Thank you, my friend."

After returning home, I walked into the trapper's shed, where Dad was skinning the days catch. His diligent attempt to perform that job seemed tedious due to the obvious mood the day had captured. He put down the knife when he realized my presence. Looking at me with obvious concern, he explained how difficult the next few days would be regarding the emotions Mutt's passing would generate. I attempted to explain that I knew what to expect, but wondered if Uncle Lee would rebound from his loss. My dad gave me a very serious look indicating his inability to give a yes or no answer. His lack of confidence indicated his serious concern for uncle's emotional well-being. He muttered, "I don't know if those old codgers will ever recover from or accept this loss." I had very limited experience in such matters; however, deep down I felt scared with a sense of concern that I had problems comprehending. The possible negative long-term issues were a serious concern.

Getting ready for bed, the mood seemed tense, with sharp verbal orders displayed, indicating lack of patience was overtaking our family's normal comfort zone.

Before jumping into bed, my sister and I looked out the window to count the cars and company at Uncle Lee's. All indications were that he and Martha were in good hands. Sis and I said good night, but to my surprise she very sensitively asked if I had an extra butterscotch candy, hinting she would really like one. My dad overheard her request and slowly walked back into the bedroom. He turned on the light next to the window. He sat on my sister's bed next to her pillow and also asked if I had any candies left saying it's a good time for all of us to enjoy Mutt's butterscotch candy and he yelled for my Mom to join us. The four of us sat and enjoyed my very last gift from Mutt, which symbolized comfort and pleasure. That simple gesture allowed each of us to be grateful for one another as we paid respect to a good friend.

CHAPTER 21

With us in Spirit

The following morning was greeted with reservations by the entire family. The late November weather was terrible and unfortunately typical; heavy snow mixed with sleet pounding on the windows. I was quite surprised when I walked into the kitchen and noticed that Dad was still at home and preparing breakfast. That was not typical of Dad, so it caused me to wonder if something unexpected had transpired during the night. His tired smile seemed forced this morning, which indicated he was feeling some serious concern and had reservations about facing the day. For that matter, my mom also showed indications that she also was in need of more sleep. While breakfast was being served by Mom, I asked Dad about his work. He acted as though he hadn't heard and in fact, completely ignored my inquiry. That morning there was genuine honest emotion and confusion radiating throughout our usually warm and comfortable home. Finally, it occurred to my mom that I needed some type of explanation regarding Dad not being at work. She told me Dad had called his boss and moved his two weeks vacation up a few days out of necessity. The entire morning's routine for uncle checking traps and getting ready for hunting season had obviously been compromised due to Mutt's death. Even though my father was grieving the loss of his friend, he also realized the responsibilities of checking sets regardless of circumstances. Checking sets was always considered mandatory. I was surprised when Dad directed me to put on my warm hunting pants, jacket, hat and packs instead of my normal school outfit. My parents had obviously talked over the situation and had decided to pull Sis and me out of school for the day. The events of Mutt's death and uncle's health indicated the need to be home and close as a family. It was apparent everyone was engrossed in the anticipation of a radical change in our normal lifestyle, which was going to be significantly challenged for the next few days. At that time, I had no idea how extraordinary that decision would prove to be.

After finishing breakfast, my sister had smartly sneaked upstairs and crawled back into bed for comfort, which both parents allowed with tolerance and understanding. Sis was showing signs of confusion about the change in her normal routine. I recall thinking my mom was probably going to sneak a well-deserved nap herself.

The weather didn't help Dad's disposition as he complained uncharacteristically. He seldom complained about weather. In all honesty, he rarely complained about anything except when the Dodgers or Red Wings lost!

Walking together outside ready to face the morning, we were greeted with snow, sleet and rain. Dad brushed off the car and started letting it warm up while I stood on the porch looking for evidence of uncle or Martha. Her truck was gone, but the old Nash was parked in its usual spot. When dad walked back onto the porch brushing the snow off of his jacket, I was calmly informed that uncle had been hospitalized during the evening for observation. He appeared to be all right, but needed rest because he showed signs of exhaustion and other undisclosed symptoms. Hearing that information, I felt scared and bogged down with serious doubts and confusion. I kept wondering what had transpired during the night. It must have been late, and for some strange reason I sensed I should not ask for any further explanation. My dad simply said that Martha and a few of my uncles were with Uncle Lee and told me not to worry because he was very strong for his age and would be back to normal in just a few days. I recall thinking and feeling Sis certainly had the right idea going back to the comforts of her bed.

Grabbing his gun case, my dad rustled my hair with a gesture indicating it was time to check sets, regardless of the circumstances. It probably seems selfish, I know, but the necessity for checking sets helped me understand my family's basic value system. Our family believed that leaving wildlife in traps any longer than necessary was absolutely forbidden. This difficult objective was welcomed and appeared to help Dad and I alleviate some stress. It also helped answer questions that surrounded the mass confusion that encompassed Mutt's passing, coupled with uncle's serious medical problems.

Driving out with wipers and heater turned on high, my father headed in a different direction than normal, but I kept that observation to myself. My poor father grappled for words, which seemed awkward, yet understandable. After driving a few miles, Dad simply said we were going to check Mutt's line and pull his traps before we checked uncles and mine. Dad was extremely focused on the task of driving in terrible weather, so I tried to stay in control of my emotions with thoughts swirling about uncle's health and well-being. Putting on his turn signal, Dad pulled off the highway onto an old logging road in an area I had never seen, or for that matter, even heard of. Even in my state of emotional insecurity, it suddenly occurred to me that my dad somehow knew through past experiences with Mutt exactly where we were. I was transfixed by Dad's intense uncommon mood. Driving slowly for about a mile without conversation, Dad casually mentioned that Mutt had a nice red pointing toward a location to our right. That area was covered with wet snow. The vision of that fox somehow seemed to eliminate the tension of my dad's unusual mood. Pulling the car off the dirt road and turning off the ignition, he sat staring at the trapped fox, and I knew that fox and the moment somehow represented everything wonderful about Mutt's lifestyle, coupled with his love of the outdoors.

Getting out of the car in wet, miserable weather to dispatch the fox, my father heard a vehicle and looked back down the logging road. In a few seconds, Simon's truck rounded the bend. Simon pulled up next to us with a knowing grin on his face. Simon had also seen the gorgeous red fox. Slowly getting out of the vehicle, Simon loudly greeted us with his appropriate opinion: "That fox represents everything good about Mutt's life." It seemed that my dad and Simon both agreed to let that old dog fox go. We were relishing in the fact that our friend Mutt was somehow with us in spirit watching my dad release that fox. When the fox realized it was free, it ran directly toward a small knob covered in wet snow. It stopped and turned around facing all of us. The gorgeous fox sat down and surprisingly started looking toward another higher knob about forty yards further down the road. That's when Simon said he could see another red hiding behind a larger knob from his vantage point. The sequence of events represented everything wonderful that the old codgers had experienced together their entire lives in their love of nature and wildlife. Dad and Simon also decided to release the second fox out of respect for their friend who had shared his life openly for sixty years with his mystical old friends. After that second fox was released, it was decided that Simon would check the rest of Mutt's line and pull his traps. Simon told us that Leo and

Weasel were at the hospital checking on uncle. Dad thanked him and I could see that some pressure had been lifted. Then there was some conversation between Simon and Dad that I felt was closed to my ears.

We left the area and we headed for Clayton's farm to start checking our family's line.

After unlocking the gate and pushing it forward, I returned to the car. Dad informed me it was necessary to find Clayton to explain about Mutt and uncle. We found Clayton milking cows in his very well-kept barn. Another friend had called Clayton, so he was already aware of the loss of Mutt and also with uncle's medical situation. He appeared genuinely concerned and softly thanked Dad for stopping. As we were heading out of the barn, Clayton yelled for us to stop. That old farmer walked slowly in our direction. Clayton seemed intense, so Dad waited patiently. When Clayton got close he informed Dad he had seen the Grey Ghost the evening before in the meadow overlooking the beaver pond. The size and rack on that buck had mesmerized even Clayton. He offered that he had seen several bucks on his property over the years, but nothing compared to the Grey Ghost. Clayton seemed so excited about his sighting and indicated he had also seen a ten-point buck traveling with the Ghost. That information was digested by my dad while he thanked Clayton for the information. Dad's mood was elevated with a new sense of purpose for the moment. Saying goodbye again, my father grabbed my hand squeezed it with love. As we walked toward the car we both noticed the weather had changed as the sun started peeking thru the clouds. My father seemed pleased with this new information from Clayton about the Grey Ghost, which he filed away for future use.

The morning had been filled with acts of kindness from our friends,, which my father verbalized as we drove toward our sets. The day had turned out nice, giving both of us some well-deserved relaxation that was apparently needed for my dad's sake. My father was sensitive to a fault, yet he always displayed toughness as required or needed. He was strong in his convictions, but he also was acutely aware of the need for discipline and consistency. You could always depend on Dad when life got complicated. My dad always seemed to understand the complex personalities he had to deal with every day. He had learned from uncle the definition of kindness and loyalty.

CHAPTER 22

The Ghost Near the Old Oak Tree

Making our way around our line, the conversation switched from uncle's health back to trapping and the priority of finding the Grey Ghost. We had some fur, but nothing to brag about. After checking the beaver pond, my father suggested we take a walk to scout the area for signs of the Grey Ghost. Heavy, wet snow was hanging on the trees, making our vision into the swamp difficult. Very few fresh tracks were evident due to the fresh snow; however, our walk was welcomed since we both needed exercise, as well as peace and quiet. Dad softly asked if weather conditions affected my ability to smell deer, and I replied yes. The wet and dreary weather made deer smell stronger; particularly the bucks. Dad wanted to know if I was aware of the rut. I answered yes and said I had learned about that process from uncle a few years earlier. He just smiled, with a knowing expression on his face. I informed Dad that during the rut, bucks smelled much stronger and they were less alert regarding hunters or noise. While we walked along the high ridge overlooking the beaver pond and swamp, I noticed that the kind old farmer, Clayton, had left two hay wagons near the top of a ridge. The wagons were located next to a hedgerow that ran from the end of the pond and continued into the edge of the huge swamp. The hedgerow ran uphill to the top of the ridge. The cornfield ran very close to the hay wagons. One wagon was located approximately twenty-five yards from the tip of the hedgerow. Dad said Clayton usually left his hay wagons out all winter because he didn't have any room in his barn or storage buildings. I asked dad if the ten-point buck that Clayton saw with the Ghost was normal and Dad replied, "It's a bit unusual for two huge bucks to travel together this time of year." He explained the territorial aspects of deer behavior, but said nothing would surprise him, and he had learned to expect the unexpected from the Grey Ghost. I was totally fascinated with the expertise and knowledge my father had acquired from uncle and his own personal experiences. Dad had always hunted deer either with uncle or alone.

The two of us walked toward the strategically located hedgerow while looking for rubs or any sign of deer movement. Just as we were reaching the top of a small knob which overlooked the hedgerow close to one of the wagons and the large corn field, I suddenly smelled the aroma of bucks and does together. I stopped dead in my tracks. Dad instinctively knew what was occurring, so he slowly knelt down and I did the same. Moving our heads very slowly, we scanned the area with no deer sighting. Then I was surprised as I turned my head slowly, looking deeper into the swamp. I poked my father with my elbow as two does were walking out of the swamp, heads down feeding. While we watched those does feed, my eyes slowly scanned the swamp, wondering why the smell was so strong. The breeze picked up slightly, causing the heavy snow to fall off the cedar branches. Then around thirty yards deeper into the swamp, I heard rattling and noticed snow falling off some swamp birch. There they were! The Grey Ghost was sparring with another huge buck, causing the snow to fall heavily off the branches. This practice bout with that huge ten-point was intense. The ten-point pushed and then drew back, heading into the Ghost. The Ghost seemed to get more serious after that last attempt of the ten-point. All of a sudden, the Ghost backed up ever so slightly, and then he lowered his head and charged very quickly, driving that ten-point back onto his hindquarters. The ten-point was completely shocked and appeared humbled and obviously a coward. Then the Ghost stood over his sparring partner, indicating his superiority. That performance answered his challenge. Dad was so engrossed with this activity that his face was twisted with a smile of disbelief. We were witnessing the natural ritual that bucks display when protecting their territory. The Ghost stood tall, with that huge rack glimmering in the sunlight. His dominance was even more prevalent when he slowly lowered his head, shaking his rack back and forth indicating victory and strength. I noticed the does watching that display with interest, probably not even aware that this entire process was all about them. For no apparent reason, the Ghost bounded deeper into the swamp and the other buck followed. With everything back to normal, my dad stood, reached out his arm and put it around my shoulders, and I could feel him shaking from the excitement. That memory is so ingrained in my mind that it gives me shivers just thinking about the vision of those two bucks fighting for territory. How perfect that my dad and I were able to witness this scene together. Turning around we started heading back toward the old Chevy. I noticed that Dad seemed distant and was displaying a feeling of disbelief. He eventually mentioned that we had been gifted the reality of the natural evolution of deer behavior.

As we got into the car, my father seemed preoccupied with feelings or thoughts he didn't share. With an unexpected statement about life, he simply told me that when I got older to remember that there are two things that bring out the worst in men. Those two things are women and venison, in that order. He laughed and told me I was far from having to deal with that reality but I learned over the years how correct he was. My dad always shared his wisdom with me and it has served me well. In turn, I have passed this information on when I felt it was appropriate. While driving to check other sets, I sensed Dad's mood was quite complicated with an internal struggle. I could see that he was torn by some very strong emotions that were tugging at his feelings due to the situation involving both the death of Mutt and Uncle Lee's current health situation. He always tried to keep his vulnerability close to his vest. Thankfully, we experienced openness in our relationship because we understood each other's needs, which is not always present in father-and-son relationships. That reality is usually compromised by performance expectations that neither can live up to. Reality often gets in the way of the primary premise. Understanding the differences in personalities makes relationships difficult at times. I found that fact out at a very early age, since I had expert advice from uncle, Dad and the old codgers.

That morning we had only one fox, two mink and a few rats on our line; however, that display by the Ghost had elevated and piqued my father's interest. During our ride home, discussion about the Ghost and that other buck stimulated our inherited mutual interest. Dad informed me that the smaller buck was obviously the son of the Ghost, so the gene pool in the swamp was alive and well. Even at my age, that made complete sense. He continued with an observation which I hadn't noticed, but would serve us well in the future. The observation was that the Ghost was active at eleven o'clock in the morning. That was unusual, since deer were usually bedded down by that time of day.

Pulling into the drive at noon, my concern for uncle caused some confusion without realizing or considering my father's plan for the remainder of the day. He wanted a quick lunch before heading to the hospital. I instinctively suggested we skin our catches. My dad assertively told me the skinning could wait until he visited uncle. My expectations were immature and insensitive. I asked to accompany dad to the hospital. Dad politely informed me that I was too young to visit uncle according to hospital rules. I remember thinking what a stupid rule that was!

While we put our catches in the shed, Martha was pulling into the drive. We made our way toward her truck and I couldn't help but notice that she looked unusually tired and worn, but she was radiant regardless of all the stress. She informed us that uncle was resting and doing much better. The doctor felt uncle could most likely return home tomorrow. That was great news. Then she graciously mentioned that uncle seemed depressed and lacked his usual energetic disposition. Dad asked if the codgers had visited and I know he was wondering if their visit had made any difference. She replied they were all there, including Clayton and other friends, but uncle was not really friendly and appeared distant.

Then out of the blue, she informed us that the store was being closed for three days out of respect for Mutt and his wife. Martha also inadvertently blindsided Dad by indicating that she was moving into uncle's home. Dad seemed to understand and he seemed pleased and comfortable with that revelation. He was not completely prepared and seemed upset by her assertiveness. I was surprised, but happy, as I understood some of the implications. Then I recalled Dad's wisdom about women and venison, which makes me chuckle even today.

My parents cleaned up after lunch, leaving me to watch Sis. She wanted to go down to the neighbors, which my parents arranged by phone. That gave me a chance to run next door to visit with Martha. Walking toward uncle's back door, it dawned on me that I should probably knock before entering. Things were already changing rapidly. Walking up the steps, Martha opened the door asking where my sister was. She obviously realized I was responsible for Sis when my parents left for a few hours. I explained about the neighbors, so she seemed satisfied. She asked me inside while she prepared tea and some lunch for herself, realizing I must have eaten at home. She graciously offered some tea and cookies and I accepted. She sat next to me with her blue cup, napkin and plate. She had inadvertently forgotten mine, so I simply got up and helped myself. I was aware of her lack of sleep and obvious concern. There was also pressure over Mutt's death and uncle's emotional and uncommonly negative, yet normal reaction.

Sitting at the table overlooking the hounds, I broke the silence and asked why she hadn't moved into uncle's before now? She took a sip of tea, wiped her mouth with the blue napkin and looked me straight in the eyes. She licked her lips and started finishing her version of the confusing relationship she had with my uncle.

Martha started explaining that after making arrangements for her fox jacket, hat and scarf, they had decided to meet after school every day near an area located just inside the woods off the path. That worked for a few months, but her father was suspicious of her activities and she never told uncle. During their meetings, uncle would talk about his life, which intrigued her. The comfort and calmness of his presence was new to her, causing strong emotional feelings that she hadn't expected and had problems understanding completely. There was little doubt that Lee was his own man with very strong opinions about life in general.

Then Martha explained that their relationship was based on his understanding of values she hadn't had to deal with because she was a product of comfort and wealth. She went on, explaining that her parents expected her to marry someone appropriate who could help her manage their business and be accepted in the social aspects required for status in the community. She was expected to attend college and go on to live a life filled with luxury and comfort. "Your uncle didn't meet those requirements. He worked hard to keep his family warm, safe and well fed, which was a tough job during those days. He only had his mule, traps and hounds which he cherished, as they served him well, thus helping him create a consistent form of income," she said. "Your uncle was very artistic and creative, which helped him survive in a world that required survival instincts not present or required in today's world." Then she explained that I had to remember that this was taking place around 1898. Horse and buggy was the means of transportation and there was no electricity available. Things were different in those days. "Your uncle never seemed completely comfortable with having to avoid being noticed or seen in public, and I knew some difficult decisions would have to be made eventually if our relationship was going to succeed," she explained.

"Everything went well for the first month or so, but the inevitable raised its ugly head around Easter that year. My dad saw me walking into a barn where your uncle and I met every chance we got. Fortunately, my dad was afraid of your uncle, so he didn't confront him, but relegated me to the house or his business and also assigned a lady friend to escort me in all social aspects of life.

Your uncle was upset with that situation and the only contact we had were letters and messages delivered by Mutt. Mutt was your uncle's best friend and he was still in school, so we communicated through Mutt and letters. Your uncle's letters were never written. He only sent sketches which illustrated his emotional pain."

"One afternoon on Good Friday, I was in church sitting alone when I felt a presence. Your uncle sat down in the pew next to me. He reached out his hand and while taking mine he simply said, 'Martha, it's your life; make your own decisions.'

Then, your uncle simply kissed me on the cheek and left after he walked confidently toward the altar. Setting a handful of flowers on the altar steps, he genuflected out of respect and then he simply walked out of the church. I was so beaten and insecure I was motionless and paralyzed. There were very few people in church at the time; however, they all recognized the significance of his gesture of love. I was so shaken by his presence and gesture of commitment that I sat alone, sobbing uncontrollably. I was feeling trapped and afraid of the consequences of having to make that decision at seventeen years old. I didn't sleep for days, and then one day during school Mutt handed me a letter from your uncle. Inside the huge envelope was a sketch of himself walking with his hound down a path he called Orchard Path which you, Ray, named the Dusty Trail, where there was apparently a huge old oak tree. He depicted himself walking with an old hound with the sun radiating on them. Under that portrait he wrote, 'Rarely have I seen anyone fail taking this path, so that's where I've been and will continue to go. I feel sorry that you are unable to make a honest decision that will make you happy later in life.'"

Martha stopped talking, stood up, wiping her eyes, and excused herself as she started upstairs for sleep. Walking up the old staircase, she told me she would finish her message when the opportunity allowed. I said, "That's all right, you need and deserve some sleep." Leaving the house, I once again walked toward my hounds, realizing the significance of the Dusty Trail and that huge old oak. My confusion was confronted by Freckles and the old redbone that sat with an understanding presence he always carried in his old, yet understanding personality. How I loved those hounds during moments like that. I released both hounds and headed toward the Dusty Trail and the huge old oak that I felt would comfort me in this confused emotional state. I wasn't scared or unhappy; just confused about women and venison, in that order! As the three of us walked in the wet snow toward the old oak I was filled with complex questions that surrounded my uncle's life. He had obviously been confronted with problems and major decisions regarding his life at a very early age. I really wanted to understand his past; yet I realized my inability to comprehend was probably normal. Uncle Lee and Martha's relationship had been on and off, so it seemed to me it was always made difficult due to circumstances neither one of them could or wanted to change.

The old redbone seemed very uncommonly nervous as we headed toward the huge oak that afternoon. Freckles, for that matter, also appeared a bit strange. When we arrived at the base of the oak they really began to act frantic. Their mood was causing me to feel very uncomfortable. I slowly looked around for some indication or answer to their behavior. I had never felt insecure before in this area but it certainly felt eerie. For some strange reason, I decided to walk a bit further down the ridge but the hounds wouldn't follow me!

Then I was shocked to see an older man walking up the ridge toward us carrying a cane which he appeared to rely on for security and support. He looked vaguely familiar. In fact, he looked just like my dad and uncles. At this point, my hounds didn't bark or seem threatened. They just acted different. Then, the old man stopped, looked my way and suddenly the rays of the sun were shining directly upon him illuminating his presence creating an appearance of serenity. The rays were revealing a soft, glowing smile on his face which I recognized as peace and comfort. He walked toward the old redbone and reached down to acknowledge my pet. That old redbone laid down with difficulty, but he appeared mesmerized by this older man's presence. Freckles walked toward the stranger and also appeared humbled. I was getting very confused by their actions, but I just stood there locked in a trance of the sensations this man was creating. I felt the warmth and security I was always conscious of when I was around my uncle, Dad and his brothers.

The older man was dressed in a hunting jacket that was well worn. He had on old jeans like mine; however, he was wearing black rubber packs. He also wore a cap slightly tipped back on his head, giving him the appearance of extreme confidence. Finally, I forced myself to say, "Hello," but the man kept petting the hounds. Then, the man slowly turned in my direction and started walking toward the oak. He simply walked right past me without any acknowledgement of my presence. When he reached the base of the oak, he looked around and leaned on his cane. Without any effort he twisted his frame strangely which appeared impossible, yet he moved gracefully toward a huge boulder some distance from the oak. Somehow this encounter was very spooky at best. Then, the man took his cane and drew a large circle in the snow and wrote my name in the middle of the circle! Suddenly, I heard a baby cry to my left and I quickly glanced in that direction. When I looked back, the man was gone and all evidence of his presence had vanished. The only thing remaining was the circle in the snow with my name written in the center.

CHAPTER 23

The End of a Relationship

The sequence of events which transpired early that afternoon caused me some serious confusion. The worst thing was that I didn't feel comfortable sharing my experience with anyone. The vision of that older man, along with Mutt's death, made it necessary for me to sort out the problems I was having difficulty accepting. Understandably, these events had evoked deep questions in my fragile well-being. The experience I had at the huge oak tree felt very much like a daydream; yet I completely understood the emotional dynamics of the circumstances. Although the vision I had just experienced seemed unrealistic and dreamlike, I found myself forced to accept the physical presence which was validated by graphic evidence still present in the snow. I was dealing with multiple events that were evoking very unusual perceptions of life I had yet to experience.

Both hounds seemed shaken and at the same time they also appeared strangely docile. Neither of them was anxious to leave the area of that old oak. They just sat there looking perplexed. I wasn't aware of nor did I care what time it was until I heard my father calling my name. He was walking down the Dusty Trail heading in our direction. He knew exactly where we had gone by following our tracks. Seeing Dad was a welcome and comforting vision. I realized the need to protect uncle's integrity, so I was forced to remain silent about the profound significance of this location. I avoided any conversation, or for that matter, any reference to what I had seen. This location wasn't strange to Dad, but I had been sworn to secrecy by Uncle Lee not to ever disclose its significance. Uncle's chiseled tribute was well hidden and buried under my feet. Having to keep this information from my father was extremely difficult because I surely could have used some understanding and support at the time. I knew if I started explaining my encounter I would face intense interrogation. I wasn't prepared for that and I didn't want to deal with any judgment or disbelief.

Walking toward Dad to prevent him from seeing the circle still present in the snow, my mood changed quickly when he excitingly informed me that uncle was home and having lunch. That information greatly improved my mood, so the four of us walked briskly back toward home. I was hoping some semblance of order would somehow magically change the crisis our family was experiencing. In retrospect, nothing that had transpired during the day seemed to represent or resemble normality. After reaching home, I leashed both hounds and quickly ran into the kitchen to greet my uncle. As I walked into the kitchen, uncle smiled at me and reached out his hand for mine. I lovingly hugged him, letting all of my suppressed feelings flow. He knew and understood that because he also seemed to need loving reassurance from me. I was extremely happy because as I took a good look at his face, I noticed that he really didn't appear any worse for wear. I don't know what I was expecting, but that reunion really pleased me and I was both grateful and surprised. I wasn't alone in my feelings. Everyone was excited to have him home and the overall mood was elevated by his mere presence.

Martha and Mom were in the living room talking about Mutt's wake and funeral, which allowed my sister to crawl onto uncle's lap without any dispute. She always anticipated or sensed the ability to take advantage of camouflage. Uncle welcomed her attempt with a smile of understanding. That moment was very gratifying for the three of us. He pulled on a pigtail, showing affection, and whispered, "It's so nice being loved by you kids." My sis reached into her pocket and handed my uncle a get well card she had proudly created herself. I read the card and noticed she had misspelled some words. The most graphic and significant part of the card was her depiction of the Grey Ghost. It was stick-like and she had drawn antlers so large they didn't fit on the paper. When uncle realized her attempt, he sat there mesmerized for a few moments, and then folded the card and placed it in his jacket pocket. While uncle thanked my sister by kissing her on the forehead, he looked up slowly toward the stairs. My father had evidently gone up there and was preparing for the wake being held at Mutt's home in a few hours.

All of a sudden, Martha walked into the kitchen and made a suggestion that uncle should stay home and not attend the wake. She told him he needed his rest. Martha was met shockingly with intense opposition by Uncle Lee. He gently put Sis on the floor and then stood up briskly and simply said, "Martha, Mutt was my best friend for over sixty-five years, so don't expect me to miss out on paying respect to his family. Mutt was always there for me when I needed him, so I see this act of respect as an absolute necessity. Don't even mention my need for rest again. Someday, down the road I hope to rest in peace myself." I could tell that he was extremely angry by her insensitive suggestion and it was obvious that Martha was agitated, as well. She softly muttered something about his attitude which I couldn't quite make out. Then, I definitely heard Uncle inform her that if she didn't approve of his attitude she could take a flying leap. My sister rescued Martha by giggling at uncle's assertiveness. Dear Cindy always had poor timing. Martha meekly walked back into the living room. That display has always given me some insight into my uncle's ability to stand his ground when he felt threatened. He obviously wasn't finished, because he followed her into the living room to further explain his position. I overheard him telling Martha that Mutt had always been there for him when the chips were down, regardless of his own personal problems. The dynamics of his relationship with Mutt was deeper and more complex than she would ever know, so he was certainly going to attend Mutt's wake regardless of what she thought would be in his best interest. Then he simply said, "Martha, it amazes me how you have always displayed a convenient memory." That conversation was stopped abruptly when Dad started heading downstairs. I was transfixed on this surprisingly assertive display of stubbornness by my uncle. He had obviously regained some insight and must have made some type of decision while he laid resting in the hospital.

My mom was ready to speak up in Martha's defense, but stopped when she heard Dad start down the stairs. Then my uncle turned toward Martha with a firm look on his face and simply said, "It's not fair for the privileged to judge the decisions that have to be made for the survival of lives that us average people have to deal with every day." This blunt statement was directed towards Martha's apparent comfortable lifestyle. Uncle simply said that during his life nothing had come easy, so having to deal with grief and sadness wasn't new to him, and he was sick and tired of outsiders thinking they knew what was in his best interest. I could see that Dad was shocked as Martha left the house. That's when uncle explained, "Nobody will ever diminish my life or my friend's reputation, especially someone who feels superior from sliding through life comfortably with money and so-called social status."

My mom softly asked what went wrong between Martha and him that had caused this apparent conflict between them. He seemed nervous, but continued explaining his position.

Apparently, while sitting in the hospital, Martha had told uncle she wanted to tear down his home and build a more suitable house similar to what she was accustomed to. She had also insulted my uncle by inferring that his home was very old and needed upgrading. He laughed with that revelation pouring out and then he offered even more information. He hugged my mom and said that old house was filled with love and kindness which always gave him comfort regardless of what he was dealing with in life. The entire family had been raised with love and values that money just couldn't buy. To imply and diminish his entire life, degrading his effort to raise his sister's children, who he felt were heads above her, or for that matter, any member of her family, was the absolute last straw. He said he realized there was no room in his life for prestige or phony social expectations.

"My name is Lee and I'm not some self-righteous arrogant pillar of the social bull crap and social scene she is accustomed to," he said. "You can't change the stripes on a skunk, no matter how hard you try. I realize it's sad how it's ending up, but Martha's expectations about comfort and luxury just do not cut it. I'm happy with what I have, which is love and respect from my family and friends. I won't compromise that security because of selfishness." That explanation just floored my parents and they said they were very sorry for any interference. Uncle politely said, "Thank you," and reminded my parents to remember who they are and fight to hold true to honesty and understanding of what always generates loyalty and respect. I was totally torn and obviously shocked with uncle's decision at that moment, which once again brought another complication to the day's events.

Both of my parents seemed shocked with this new twist; however, both of them were surprisingly more relaxed than upset. Their acceptance helped Sis and I feel more secure than we had felt a few moments ago while everything was transpiring. At the same time, it seemed strange to me that within a few seconds the entire future of two people could change forever. That performance from my uncle will always remind me of how fragile relationships can be. Once again, I recalled Dad's message regarding women and venison.

Uncle left to get cleaned up and ready for the wake. He asked Mom if she would press his shirt if it needed it. She graciously told him she had already done so and told him it was hanging next to his suit. Then my mother told uncle she had also tied a double Windsor knot in his maroon tie. They hugged with affection before he slowly walked away to possibly reflect and make an attempt to accept the consequences of what had just transpired.

My parents seemed very emotional after witnessing the death of a relationship plus the real death of a very close friend. My sister once again added her lighthearted perspective by asking if I had any more butterscotch candy. Both parents laughed at her lack of understanding, and Dad lifted her up into his arms saying, "My God Cindy, you're a gift that keeps on giving." Mom simply patted her with love and affection.

With everyone ready to leave for Mutt's wake, my mother took inventory of their clothing, admiring how handsome both uncle and Dad were. They were both dressed up with Stetson hats and their Harmony Black suits. I was given some last-minute instructions by Dad. Then Mom reminded me if any problems occurred, all I needed to do was pick up the phone and tell the operator (who was my Aunt Nancy) to get me help. To be frank, nothing would have surprised me after having experienced that day's events. With the three of them heading down the street in Uncle's old Nash, I was filled with a feeling of loneliness which was quickly eased when my sister suggested we bring Freckles and the old redbone into the house to warm up. I loved my sister's ability to have her priorities straight regardless of total confusion.

CHAPTER 24

Funeral for a Friend

After going outside in the bitter cold to fetch the two hounds and bring them into the warm house, my sister and I felt safe and secure. Those hounds somehow understood their roles in bringing some badly needed diversion from the tremendous complications that had transpired that day. While Sis played with her paper dolls, I just laid down and listened to music on the radio. The music was provided by somebody named Lawrence Welk. I usually preferred country music, but the Lawrence Welk music was more uplifting, so there was no reason to change channels. Both hounds curled up next to the wood stove for warmth and comfort, so I simply crawled between in an attempt to rearrange my baseball cards. My sister slowly turned toward me and innocently asked if I thought Martha would ever return after the argument. I was very surprised by her observation and her apparent understanding of the potential consequences of what transpired that afternoon. She told me that Martha and she had played Old Maid alone one afternoon while mom did the laundry. Evidently, Martha had told my sister she badly needed several new appropriate outfits for school, which she intended to buy. That insensitive and degrading remark was an indication of very poor judgment on Martha's part. Her observation regarding my parents' diligent attempt to provide pretty dresses and outfits for my sister gave me some insight about Martha's true colors and lack of sensitivity. Apparently, uncle always had to deal with Martha's constant quest for luxury during their turbulent relationship. That characteristic had always been an issue. I recalled uncle saying one afternoon in the trapper's shed that charity began at home. I remember thinking that was probably what he meant by that statement. It was during that revelation by sis that I decided to confront my uncle when appropriate about the other side of Martha's personality.

The phone rang, so I reluctantly got up to answer. Saying hello, I found myself talking to my Aunt Nancy, the operator, who was calling to check on Sis and me. The concern shown by my aunt validated my uncle's perception of family values that he alone had instilled in the entire extended family. Simply holding care and concern close to the heart, as displayed by a family member, indicated that uncle's benchmark for values was paying dividends. He delicately preached when he felt the time was right or relevant that values were expected to be displayed within the entire family dynamics. I also recalled my uncle explaining ever-so-carefully how difficult it was to teach an old dog new tricks, along with not being able to change the stripes on a skunk.

Crawling back between the hounds for warmth, the entire process of accepting life on life's terms became entrenched in my young personality and normal maturation process that was being comprehended reluctantly that afternoon.

I rolled over asking my sis if she would throw me a pillow from the couch. In her typical style, she got up slowly and reached for the small tan pillow with a smirk on her freckled face. I was instantly sorry for my request. Sis threw the pillow, messing up my baseball cards, and the war was on. God knows how badly that show of love between us was needed. It helped us to release pent up feelings and energy. The fight also helped remove some stress from our young vibrant bodies. The two hounds never moved; they both watched patiently understanding the fight was about love between a brother and sister. The only problem this encounter created was when we tipped over a photograph of uncle sitting at his desk next to that old owl. Thank God it wasn't broken, which seemed to prove that uncle was always involved in our lives, even during his absence.

After picking up the paper dolls and baseball cards and arranging the pillows back on the couch, my sister slowly walked upstairs with Freckles following. Sis yawned and informed me she was headed for bed. With Sis upstairs in bed, the redbone and I laid on the couch listening to the radio. Just before I turned the channel our local announcer named Gene started the local news and it always included recent deaths in the area. That tradition was always announced at the end of the broadcast, so I listened intently.

Mutt was seventy-three, a year older than uncle, and he had married Pearl at the age of twenty. They had one child that died at the age of four from polio and were both very active in the March of Dimes. He had worked at the plant as a carpenter after graduating from high school. Mutt and his wife were very active in their church and each of them were members of several community organizations. The announcer also revealed that Mutt had played hockey in his youth and baseball on the traveling teams that represented the village in the Valley League. Gene also emphasized the fact that Mutt was an avid outdoorsman, and I felt that was a great comment to mention. After the news, I turned off the radio and curled up next to the redbone, realizing how significant that old hound had been over the years giving me comfort any time I needed it.

It wasn't long after lying down that I heard the car drive in and the doors slam. Shortly after hearing my parent's car, I heard uncle's Nash pull beside the trappers shed and his door slam indicating everyone was home safely. My parents walked into the kitchen and they both took inventory of the house. Neither of them mentioned the hounds being inside. They seemed tired and appeared as if they were both happy this day was coming to an end. Dad removed his jacket and tie, asking if Sis was in bed. I said, "Yes, with freckles," and he smiled. Turning toward Mom, he told her he had to go next door to help uncle write something called a eulogy.

Mom said, "That's nice-don't hurry." Dad left for next door and Mom told me to go upstairs and get ready for bed. Walking slowly upstairs with Mom close behind, I was filled with questions, but didn't have the nerve to ask at the time. During prayers, I remember thinking that I suddenly understood why nightly prayers were important, because doing so gave me comfort and peace. Prayers weren't just a nightly ritual, they actually helped sooth my emotions. After tucking me into bed, Mom calmly asked if I would be willing to play a small role in Mutt's funeral. She went on to say that my participation was suggested by Mutt's wife and she and Dad thought it would please everyone if I agreed. With that endorsement and commitment from Mom, I surely didn't have the nerve to say no. Mom kissed me good night and checked on Sis and Freckles, who was still lying at my her feet. Before heading downstairs, my mom told me that uncle was his normal self and appeared in complete control of his feelings.

I rolled over and looked out the window and saw Dad and uncle sitting at the kitchen table talking, and they were both smiling. Those two men always made the best out of a bad situation. With that picture in my mind, I curled up, pulled the blankets up under my chin and slowly drifted off to sleep.

The following morning was hectic as Dad responded to phone calls from family members and some curiosity-seekers, which he sorted out easily. Arrangements were made for Sis to go to a neighbor's house during the funeral and while mom talked to her friend, she pressed a dress for herself and then pressed Dad's new white shirt, along with his suit pants. I heard mom say Pearl had asked to have my dad and his brothers serve as pallbearers and the cronies were designated honorary pallbearers. I also heard every member of the hockey and baseball teams that Mutt had played on asked to sit together out of respect. After Mom hung up, she decided to finish making a breakfast consisting of bacon and eggs served with toast and some orange juice. I noticed that my Sunday clothes weren't laid out, so I asked what I was expected to wear. Mom just explained I wouldn't need my Sunday best. That confused me, but I knew that mothers always knew best.

With mass confusion in our home, I really didn't have time to think much about my clothes, or for that matter, my small role in the service. I found out that uncle was going to escort Pearl during the service, along with just a few of their relatives. They were from a very small family. I was shocked when I heard my uncles pull up and get out of their cars. They all looked sharp and seemed prepared for the honor of participating in their friend's final goodbye. The fact that every male member of our family would be taking a significant part in this funeral was extremely symbolic. Little did I realize how meaningful that request was. That gesture by Pearl was more significant than even she realized. With everyone ready and prepared, the family got into the cars and headed towards Mutt's home. The funeral director wanted everyone at Mutt's early to arrange the procession and to give everyone their last-minute instructions. That process included me.

With everything organized, I walked toward Pearl, who was standing alone on her porch. Pearl was dressed in black with one exception. I noticed a broach on her long, black dress coat; the broach of a fox that had diamonds for eyes. It was gorgeous and appropriate for the mood and circumstances. She was very somber and tired. Pearl looked as if she was in shock, but she leaned over and took my hand, saying that Mutt would be so very happy with my role honoring his memory. I was sad, but I explained that uncle would watch over her and I told her not to worry because her friends would see to it that she would be fine. Then I offered to shovel her drive and sidewalk during the winter and she smiled at my childlike attempt to help. With everyone ready and accounted for, we got into the vehicles and waited for Pearl to say goodbye to Mutt for one last time. No one uttered a word. They all sat with heads down out of respect. Pearl said her final goodbyes, and then walked outside. Uncle put out his arm, which she took thankfully, and they both walked slowly toward her car. While the funeral director and my uncles carried the casket and placed it into the hearse, Pearl averted her eyes so as to avoid having that final scene in her memory.

Turning the lights of the vehicles on, we slowly drove down the street heading for the Congregational Church, and to everyone's surprise, the entire police force stood at attention saluting at the end of Mutt's street. That display had been organized by my other uncle, who was a cop. The motorcade continued to make its way toward Main Street. The entire community was stopped dead in their tracks as this long precession worked its way toward the church.

While the details were sorted out of getting the congregation seated and preparing for Pearl and uncle to escort the casket, I was taken by Mom into the social hall to get me prepared for my role in the service. My mom seemed very placid, yet she also displayed some sense of peace. I heard organ music indicating the service was ready to start. Mom and I slowly walked outside and waited for everyone to be placed properly in their pews. Then we walked quickly toward the sanctuary to wait for our cue. While Mom and I waited, a white truck pulled into the parking lot of the church. As Mom realized who it was, her entire attitude changed immediately as she walked toward her friend. Martha got out of her vehicle and graciously smiled in my direction, which made me feel both empty and sad. When Mom took Martha's hand, Martha started to cry out of grief for Mutt and probably feeling alone and lost realizing the consequences the confrontation she had with uncle the day before. My mother walked Martha to the church, hugged her and returned to me, standing outside alone and appearing torn as a result of the heated conversation that had taken place the day before in our home. When Mom got within hearing distance of me, I bluntly asked if Martha was all right. Mom understood and just replied that the entire situation is complicated, and we didn't have time to discuss this matter now. She said, "It's time for you to take your place in the sanctuary."

Once inside the sanctuary, I was given an Easter basket full of butterscotch candies from the funeral director that I was to hand out as I made my way down the aisle. I was expected to take a seat behind Pearl and uncle. Before my cue, the door to the sanctuary was opened and my cousin handed me my hunting jacket to wear, along with my red hunting hat. With my clothes changed and basket in hand, my cousin opened the door again and walked inside the sanctuary with the old redbone on a leash. Mom left for her seat and I waited for my cue. The organist started playing "Amazing Grace," so I walked nervously into the back of the church, holding the basket of butterscotch candy in one hand. I unleashed the redbone and he stayed at my side. While the music played, I walked down between the pews handing out the candy while that old redbone walked alongside. The entire congregation was moved with this unique display of love and respect. I could feel the entire attitude inside that church change as we slowly walked down the aisle. The minister surprised me when he walked down the altar steps toward me and the red-bone hound. Standing in front of the congregation, he took a candy, unwrapped it and put it in his mouth. Then he patted the hound and walked back toward the pulpit. The significance of that effort was so spiritual the organist began crying and as a result had problems playing the music.

The service was pleasant and very appropriate, and then the time came for my uncle's attempt to give his eulogy. I sat transfixed on the moment when uncle stood up confidently and walked toward the pulpit. He patted the casket as he walked by and reached down and patted the redbone, who tried to follow. To my surprise, he took the hound and the two of them stood together at the pulpit. Taking a very deep breath, my uncle started his message. He explained that he had lived next door to Mutt for twenty-six years and they had been raised like brothers from the time they were around two years old. With both families struggling, they had helped each other survive during very difficult times. They shared gardens and work required to survive during those years. Uncle explained that Mutt was very smart and worldly, which complemented their relationship. Mutt's abilities were too numerous to mention, but his loyalty and work ethic were admirable. Then my uncle stated that his friend of over seventy years had evolved into a tremendous athlete in his youth, along with skills he had learned which were unmatched in the knowledge of nature. Apparently, they grew up closer than brothers, giving everyone the impression that they actually were brothers, which they often pretended to be. The relationship continued to evolve with Mutt always thinking of others first before himself. Uncle Lee explained that he had been the best man at Pearl and Mutt's wedding, which had been a great honor. Then uncle mentioned the death of Mutt and Pearl's son, because my uncle was the godfather of that child. He explained that his friends were devastated, but Pearl pulled everything together like she always did. The entire congregation sat transfixed by uncle's description of Mutt's life, and in conclusion, he said that Mutt was a gentleman, but more importantly, a kind and gentle man. Then uncle left the pulpit walking toward Pearl and he gently kissed her on the forehead.

While walking toward Pearl, uncle had noticed someone in the back of the church standing alone, so he walked toward that person. As uncle walked assertively toward the back of the church everyone turned around. Walking Charlie was nervously standing alone in the back of the church. Uncle took Charlie's hand and he brought him down the aisle and seated him with Pearl and himself. Needless to say, tears were really flowing. Charlie was happy and displayed his butterscotch candy, raising a handful into the air, and everyone laughed out of respect.

With the service over, my uncles started out of the church carrying the casket to the music of "Onward Christian Soldiers," but they stopped dead in their tracks as the organist started playing "Take Me Out to the Ballgame" which Mutt's teammates sang along out of respect for their friend. That overwhelming tribute was the final gesture displayed during the service for my friend Mutt.

CHAPTER 25

Emotional Times for All

W ith the service finally over, everyone appeared relieved. The emotions felt during the service were intense, with some normal reservations about the tough act of placing and burying Mutt in the cemetery. That whole process seemed so morbid and unnecessary from my perspective. I continued to question that process while I watched Uncle Lee support Pearl as they stood next to the casket placed over the grave. On the other side of the casket, the codgers were all in place next to Martha, who was standing alongside Simon, Weasel and Leo. Martha was softly weeping and wringing her hands with nervousness. It was obvious she was wretched with grief. I thought she looked extremely tired and sad, which started making me think a bit more compassionately about her and the complicated events of the past few days. My other uncles and my dad stood respectfully behind Pearl and uncle. It was impossible not to notice how significant the display of solidarity and deep emotion was affecting each of us as we were laying a friend and husband to rest. With the final prayers being said, everyone left the grave and stood around the cars discussing the funeral process along with fond memories of Mutt and his lovely wife.

As all of my uncles and aunts milled around hugging each other, it was obvious Martha wasn't anywhere to be seen. Dad walked over in my direction and grabbed my hand. He told me he was bursting with pride as he watched me walk respectfully down the aisle with the candy and redbone at my side. To be totally honest, at that moment I just wanted the hell out of the graveyard. Dad understandably realized my feelings and yelled to Mom, indicating it was time to leave. Suddenly, Pearl and uncle appeared with Martha, also walking on the other side of Pearl for moral support. Uncle helped Pearl into a vehicle, along with her chosen family members, and they simply closed the car door, drove out of the graveyard and turned in the direction of home. My uncle was visibly shaken and turned slowly toward Martha. He indicated he wanted to go back to the grave. Walking slowly, he hollered to the entire family to join him again at the grave. No one knew what to expect, yet we all reluctantly headed toward Mutt's casket.

With everyone standing once again around the grave, my uncle raised his hand and removed his dress hat out of respect. His nephews all followed suit, as did the other family members who were present. Uncle simply said, "This entire family will always cherish Mutt and Pearl. Then he looked toward the heavens and said, "Mutt, from this day forward, our family will always honor your wife as part of this family. Isn't that right everyone?" At that time someone said let us pray and the entire family said The Lord's Prayer in unison. Then we simply turned and left Mutt's grave. We all said our goodbyes, got into our cars and headed for home.

During the ride home, my father explained that there were only two occasions in his recollection when the family had chosen to adopt a member outside of the family to be treated as one of us. Our already huge family had just gained another significant member who became one of us because she needed our help and support. Mom simply said that this tradition was awesome and it made her feel safe and secure and proud to be part of our family.

Getting Sis from the neighbor's home, all four of us were again reunited. We simply drove into our drive, exited the car and walked slowly inside the modest home Dad had provided for us out of his love and hard work.

While changing my clothes, I heard uncle drive up in his Nash next to the trapper's shed. I looked out the window and watched him walk slowly into the garage. I assumed he was probably going to start a fire in the stove located in the back of the shed before changing his clothes. I quickly undressed, hoping I was correct in my assumption.

When I got downstairs, Dad was already changed and he informed me he had to drive to Clayton's to pick up some fur. Apparently, one of Clayton's workers had checked our line that morning after milking. Dad explained that the old farm hand had offered to check our line out of respect for Uncle Lee, who had helped him out of trouble a year ago. That farm hand hadn't had the opportunity to repay uncle. His gesture of kindness was an indication of the respect my uncle had earned from simply being kind. I asked Dad if it was okay if I stayed home and he agreed, probably knowing I was going to join uncle in the shed. Dad was certainly very perceptive when it came to my sister and me.

Dad drove down the street and I suddenly realized he probably wanted to be alone to collect his thoughts and put everything into perspective.

I went out back to check on the hounds and I heard uncle close his door as he walked in our direction. I asked him out of concern how he felt and he responded, "Okay." Then he added, "To be honest, Ray, I am feeling a bit empty." Then he said he would like me to join him in the trapper's shed. The fire in the wood stove was radiating heat that felt so good and smelled comforting. Uncle sat in the recliner, so I simply sat on my stool next to the workbench.

Taking a long, deep breath, he removed his glasses and rubbed his tired face and eyes. While running his hands through his hair, he said with a low whisper, "Ray, this has been a very trying, painful time in my life. I've been faced with difficult times before, but the older I get it, seems harder and harder to muster up the energy to handle such emotional times." I somehow knew there was more information coming. I always knew he wanted and needed to vent his deep feelings during times like this.

Then he asked if I realized the consequences of the past three days and wondered if I needed some explanation regarding the chain of events that had transpired. I took a few moments, not knowing where to start first.

Then I simply said, "Uncle Lee, your relationship with Martha makes me sad, because you both seem to need and love each other. So why do the two of you make it so complicated?" He lifted his head looking perplexed, so I continued, "These entire few weeks have been filled with emotions. Some were good feelings and some were bad feelings that are both very complicated; however, it seems to me that you are so much happier when Martha's around." Then I explained that Mom and Dad argued at times, but they never just walked away without some type of compromise. I could tell that he was shocked by my simple, yet profound observation.

He said, "Ray you're too young to understand all of this, so let's change the subject." Darn him, I wasn't going to let him off the hook that easy, so I informed him how his reactions at times were a contradiction to the values he instilled in us and expected us to live up to.

I went on to say that I had heard a particular saying in Sunday school: "Do as I say; not what I do." He suddenly got defensive, raising his hand to stop me from continuing. I quickly said, "You're being stubborn and unfair!" Then I said, "All right, we can change the subject. I would like to explain something that happened to me the other day down the Dusty Trail at the huge oak that scared me out of my wits." I was grateful that he listened because I needed to describe the encounter with that mysterious stranger that looked so familiar. After I went through all of the details, Uncle sat up straight and wiped his brow with his handkerchief and told me to continue describing the experience. I explained the chain of events I had witnessed in detail again. Then, without any warning, uncle asked how the man wore his cap and if he had on black packs. From that question I knew instantly that he knew the man, so I asked who the man was.

With apparent confusion, my uncle walked toward me, grabbed my shoulders and looked me straight in the eyes. He shook his head and replied, "Ray, I'm sorry I put you in this position at such a very early stage in your life."

I was scared, yet curious so I asked another question. "Was that man real or was I dreaming?"

Uncle said, "He's real, but please don't divulge that experience to anyone other than me." Man, there was no winning with my uncle today.

All of a sudden, uncle said he was extremely tired and needed a nap. That was a clue for me to leave the shed, but before I left I simply said, "Uncle, you're carrying a burden inside that has to get out, just like you told me the day you found me down the Dusty Trail after the confrontation with my teacher. You told me to get it out and everything would be okay. Do you remember saying that?" I turned and started walking out of the shed thinking about needing a nap myself. Before leaving the shed, I turned and reminded him that hunting season opened today and that Dad expected him to be ready in the morning to hunt the Grey Ghost. The realization of the trauma that my uncle was dealing with hit me straight in the pit of my stomach. I recall thinking how simple life was before when all I was concerned with was playing with my buddies and hounds. Back then, life was devoid of living responsibilities and adult relationships. I turned and walked toward the hounds and the safety of home.

Inside the comfort of home, Mom asked if uncle was all right and I said, "I think so," with a delivery that must have revealed some problem she may have seen coming. She walked toward me with concern, knelt down and gave me a warm hug that was badly needed. I felt safe and loved, so I intently explained that uncle was difficult to deal with regarding his own personal life and feelings. I told her that I wondered why he always seemed so concerned about everyone else, but ignored his own happiness. She told me to go upstairs and take a nap before supper. She obviously had something to do that she felt was very important. As I climbed onto my bed, I heard the front door slam and saw that Mom was walking toward the trapper's shed wearing Dad's hunting jacket. Mom was on a mission, which indicated that she was going to have a heart-to-heart conversation with my uncle. Then Dad pulled into the drive, so Mom turned and waited for him to join her. They talked for a minute or two and then they both walked toward the shed while Dad hitched up his pants just like Uncle Lee. The entire mood of this day was reaching a climax no one could have predicted. I heard another vehicle, so I looked out the window and Martha's white truck was pulling into uncle's drive. My parents waited for her to exit and greeted her with open arms. The three of them talked for a while and then turned and walked toward the shed. Oh, how I wished I could have been a fly on the wall to hear the conversation about to take place inside that shed!

CHAPTER 26

Revelations After
all These Years

I laid down reluctantly on my bed, gripped with feelings of guilt. I felt remorseful because of my overreaction to the conversation with uncle in the trapper's shed which had upset Mom. In the past, she had always allowed uncle and me the luxury of our privacy. That day, with emotions being so high and each one of us wearing our respective heart on our sleeve, it was apparent overreaction was natural.

The past couple of days had generated extensive conflict which my mother felt was unnecessary. Mom never failed to protect my sis and I from problems that she perceived as a potential threat to our security, whether physical or emotional. I felt torn and anxious. I certainly wished I had kept my big mouth shut. Living in a family of such love and closeness also had its pitfalls. There was no need to confront uncle with additional problems which could force some serious ramifications. I have to admit that I was taking the burden my uncle was dealing with personal. I prayed that he wouldn't blame me for this intervention. After all, he needed understanding; not judgment or for that matter scolding, which Dad, Mom and Martha were highly proficient at. I had dealt with their ability to clarify their thoughts firsthand. To gang up seemed unfair and callous.

Although I was filled with doubt, I got off the bed, put on my black sneakers and walked downstairs. I decided to save my uncle from serious humiliation or emotional pain. I found myself running toward the shed without any reservation or concern about my own security or for that matter possible discipline that would probably be the end result for my interference. Running into the garage, the door to the trapper's shed opened quickly and I almost fell inside because uncle was storming out, mad as hell! When he saw me and realized my intention, he quickly told me to go home and get some warm clothes on. He said we were headed for the Dusty Trail to get away from the bull crap that none of the self-righteous do-gooders could not or would not understand. Then I looked inside the shed and saw that Mom was crying alongside Martha. Dad was just standing there alone frozen in place and he appeared shocked with uncle's reaction. That graphic display was extremely poignant, so I just ran quickly to get dressed in warmer clothes, not even considering my parents or Martha.

Uncle was still upset when he entered the kitchen to wait for me to get dressed. He assertively explained that we needed to clear the air and that the old oak was the place to resolve the issues the others obviously wouldn't accept. Uncle simply said, "If its the last thing I do, Ray, you deserve to know the truth and I realize you, of all people, will not judge or question the validity of what we need to discuss. I hope we can resolve the issues that require some explanation." My uncle was strong and vibrant and it appeared he was once again in complete control of the situation. He never wavered from his need or desire to seek and accept the truth as he understood it. I realized that what was going to be discussed would at least hopefully answer my questions and relieve some of uncle's anxiety. Walking off the porch, my uncle told me to fetch the hounds. Then he added, "Even the damn hounds are capable of realizing the simplicity of this revelation." He said, "When people insist on answers to their questions, they should expect to get answers they may not be prepared to hear or for that matter, accept. They always have a tendency to want the answers they expect."

Things were very quiet in the shed, but I honestly didn't care at that point, because I was more concerned about my uncle. At least the three of them had each other for comfort, but Uncle Lee sought me and the hounds out for his emotional needs and to air his frustrations. As we walked toward the oak with Freckles and the redbone alongside, uncle took my hand and continued walking briskly with a sense of urgency. Uncle's apparent need to clear the air was foremost on his agenda. He started picking up sticks and firewood along the way, which indicated he expected to start a small fire. That was also a clue that some time would be needed to allow him the opportunity to divulge what he obviously felt needed explaining.

While we walked, he informed me that the three of them had barged into the shed unannounced and confronted him regarding their insensitive perception of his "bizarre and unfamiliar behavior." Martha had shocked uncle by indicating that she felt he was on the verge of a nervous breakdown and my parents had sided with her inference. He went on to explain that he wasn't crazy and he cautiously indicated they weren't prepared for his explanation. He said they wouldn't relent and insisted he was showing signs and symptoms of dementia. I didn't understand the word dementia, but it obviously wasn't good and I didn't interrupt to ask. He also told me they felt he lacked the ability to think clearly. He said he told all three of them to sit down and he tried to explain the seriousness of the answers they insisted on to help them resolve their selfish, narrow-minded opinions.

After reaching the huge oak, he asked me to help find some dead branches to use as firewood which, I did quickly. With a pile of kindling wood, some heavy branches and dry leaves, he built a small fire. It was late in the afternoon, so heat and light would be needed and welcomed. The hounds seemed pleased with the warmth of the fire. That simple gesture from the hounds finally brought a smile to uncle's stern face. There was a calmness that overtook uncle, reassuring me he was in complete control of his thoughts.

Trying to ease my internal nervousness, I slowly asked why he felt it was imperative for him to include me with the information he had shared with Mom, Dad and Martha. "Ray," he offered, "your experience down here the other day validated my need to help you understand and accept it for what it was. You're young, but very intelligent, so it's really time for you to hear all the facts, because if something happens to me you'll always be tormented about what you saw down here the other day. With the fire burning well, we started brushing snow off the rocks located near that huge boulder where the fire had been started. Suddenly, we saw Dad making his way toward the oak looking for us.

When my father got closer, my uncle told him, "If you're coming here to try and stop the truth or inject more bull crap, be prepared for the shock of your life." Uncle was serious because he also said to Dad that if he wasn't prepared to accept the truth to give him back the gold pocket watch before he left. At that point I realized my uncle was seriously angry and very disappointed with my father ,and for that matter, Mom and Martha.

Dad wasn't prepared for uncle drawing a line and taking such a drastic stance, so he calmly relented and said he just wanted to join us for a few minutes, which I knew was a lie. Uncle said, "Leon, you're a great dad and husband and

I chose you as the male of this family to help keep us all together; but if you're not capable or willing to handle the truth involved with this responsibility, I will understand and accept that decision." Then uncle added sincerely that he was aware of the pressure Dad was under, but it was no excuse for indicating that uncle was losing it. Dad sat down next to me with some reservation; however, his allegiance toward uncle gave him the strength to reluctantly accept uncle's stern conditions. That was a moment of truth between the three of us that cool afternoon. My father had calmed down some, so I felt he totally accepted the fact that the need to listen might help bring the three of us back onto the same page.

Dad told uncle to start at the beginning and said he would listen with an open mind, but asked if it was necessary for me to be present. Uncle stood up and hitched his pants then started rubbing his chin while he told Dad that it was absolutely necessary. He said it would help me resolve the complications that unfortunately encompassed the past several days. Wow, Dad backed off again saying, "Okay, you're in charge."

Uncle rebutted, "I'm not in charge of anything. I just feel responsible for Ray's confusion. The purpose is to help clarify any questions he or you have about my ability to function. I want you to know I'm certainly not incompetent and ready for the old folks home yet."

The back-and-forth continued briefly until Dad finally said, "All right, start at the beginning."

That display of compromise by both alpha males really indicated how powerful their personalities were. Uncle put more wood on the fire while showing signs of very long, difficult thoughts while he prepared for his confession about our family and some significant others.

With the three of us sitting, my uncle started at the beginning. "During the time when uncle and Mutt lived next door to each other, they had been raised much like brothers. All during their childhood the two families endured terrible struggles, but survived some very difficult, trying times. Uncle and Mutt, along with their dads, had worked diligently to keep the entire neighborhood in food and proper shelter. They had both assumed the duties and responsibilities of helping every man, woman and child survive tremendous hardship during the cold and tedious winters. In fact, the small neighborhood became dependent upon those two families, regardless of their own security and safety. No one objected because it was simply the right thing to do. As Mutt and uncle got older and closer, they started playing sports and uncle introduced Mutt to the benefits of pursuing wildlife for money and survival. They never wavered from the reality that persevered during their youth. Mutt's family even helped create a small pantry which was open to the less fortunate. Mutt stayed in school because he promised his mom he would graduate. Uncle had quit school out of necessity to hunt, fish and trap, which supplied food and money for anyone that needed it."

"Their dads both worked when work was available, but jobs were scarce and difficult to find. They had worked together as close as Mutt and Uncle Lee. Their small families were joined in extremely powerful displays of family values. My uncle went on to say that his dad got sick and passed away just before Mutt met Pearl. Uncle and Martha were still in an unstable relationship because of Martha's dad during those years. It was during Martha's senior year that uncle made a decision to confront her dad and have a serious conversation with him. Uncle decided it was time to make a brave attempt to resolve their standoff and come to an agreement on some very serious issues. So, one evening my uncle said he walked into Martha's father's office to make an attempt to reach an understanding or compromise. Looking for Martha's dad, he discovered he had walked into a very difficult and embarrassing situation. He was shocked to find Martha's dad having sex in his office with a young lady. That young lady worked for Martha's dad as his bookkeeper. To complicate things, this young lady happened to be one of the neighbors who lived close to both uncle and Mutt's families. Uncle said he quickly left without being noticed; however, that situation ended his desire to attempt to face Martha's father ever again."

"About three months later, that young lady appeared to be with child and she never went to work again, which certainly wasn't hard to understand. After the baby was born, the entire neighborhood was filled with gossip and speculation about the father of her child. That poor lady and her family suffered from humiliation and judgment making their lives difficult, to say the least. The baby was a boy who seemed healthy and energetic. When the child was around four years old, he came down with scarlet fever and survived, but he suffered mild brain damage as a result of the high fever. The boy was named Charles and after his brain damage became obvious, his mom hung herself, leaving only her parents to care for him. The grandparents raised Charlie until they both passed away from the flu epidemic that killed several adults and children that year. Incidentally Ray, that was the same winter your namesake passed." Uncle said. "So, I obviously knew who Charlie's father was, but kept it to myself. The boy was homeless, so I made arrangements to pay for his room and board in a small, but good boarding institution for children in need. That went on for several years and then I assumed his guardianship and accepted the responsibility for his welfare. That boy is the half-brother Martha never knew she had. I probably should have told her, but the ramifications and repercussions were too great to take the chance. Charlie seemed happy, so I decided not to confuse his life any further. That child was nicknamed Walking Charlie and the entire village accepted and looked out for him. And, yes, it is the same Walking Charlie you have met."

After that revelation, my dad stood up, took a deep breath and said, "That explains your close relationship with Walking Charlie." He pressed for more details, but my uncle just put some more wood on the fire. I felt somewhat empty trying to digest situations which were very complicated such as this, but my uncle sat down and told us the rest of his confession would be even more significant and harder to explain. He said he would do his best to make an honest attempt.

Uncle poked at the fire and patted Freckles as he tried to collect his thoughts. He seemed very emotional, but he took a deep breath and slowly started to explain the sequence of events that had changed his life forever.

The complicated circumstances were slowly giving dad and myself some insight as to where uncle was emotionally. My uncle removed his glasses, wiped his eyes and said, "What I just told you regarding Walking Charlie had nothing to do with Martha, but it certainly caused me some serious resentments. It wasn't her fault, she simply didn't know about Charlie and I felt it was in their best interest not to divulge that information. Charlie was doing fine, he seemed happy and well cared for, so I felt I made the right decision at the time. Martha recently became very inquisitive and started asking me questions about the close relationship I had with Charlie. She sensed something about that situation. She continued to press me for information, so I chose not to keep it from her any longer. Well, now she has a serious crisis in her life. We will see how she handles this problem. It doesn't make me happy knowing after all these years I was finally forced to divulge the truth."

Uncle took a deep breath and finally said, "Let's get back to our family, which is the primary premise for this discussion. Before Mutt and I were born, our families lived next door to each other and everything was shared, including hard work, food and any other essentials needed for survival during the long, cold winters. My dad and Mutt's mom were friendly and some thought they seemed destined to marry. That never transpired because my dad was interested in Joyce and Mutt's mom was trying to attract another man. My father married your mother when she was only sixteen and Mutt's mom finally landed her catch. Everything was going along fine with normal living experiences. Remember, in those days, nothing came easy. The living conditions were rough. Living next door to Mutt's parents was helpful for my mom and dad, and Mutt's parents also relied on my parents when needed. Shortly after they married, Mutt's mom became pregnant and a year after Mutt was born, I followed. Mutt and I were so close in age we were raised like brothers while our dads worked, because work and money were scarce. They pooled their funds, shared gardens and other requirements needed for survival. As Mutt and I grew closer and older, we were inseparable. Everyone who knew us or saw us together commented and said we were closer than brothers, which was probably true."

Uncle Lee continued, "As time went on, life's problems started hitting our families fast and furious. First of all, my dad passed away from a heart attack when I was seventeen. His death was sudden, and with him gone, I felt lost for the first time in my life. I couldn't help it, but I became so angry with our maker. My father's passing left me with only my mom to worry about, but his death also made times much more difficult. Mutt's dad had to carry the burden of the neighborhood responsibilities somewhat alone without much adult help. Mutt's father was strong and healthy, along with being very gentle. The only healthy males left in the neighborhood were Mutt, his father and me. We did our best to make daily attempts to provide what we could for anyone in need. That went well for two years. Then, around Thanksgiving, Mutt met Pearl and they fell for each other and became attached at the hip. I really liked Pearl because she was smart and she was a very hard worker. I must admit she was also very pretty. Their courtship moved smoothly until Mutt's dad was unfortunately killed in a logging accident, which devastated the entire community. After his dad was killed, Mutt and Pearl got engaged. Two years went by and after Mutt graduated from high school, he was offered a job at the plant. They were doing great with a steady income, so just before Mutt's twenty-first birthday, they married, and I was honored to be their best man. Martha had already left for college, so Pearl had another girlfriend stand up as her maid of honor."

"Pearl and Mutt didn't waste any time starting a family, and it wasn't long before Pearl gave birth to a baby boy. They named him Leon, after me. They asked if I would be the godfather of that child and it was a privilege to accept. I recall helping Mutt teach little Leon to walk. I enjoyed interacting with my godchild every chance I had. The process which we shared completely solidified our friendship and love for our families. During that time my sister had married at sixteen and they started pumping out children. By the time I was twenty, they had four boys and one girl. Obviously, Leon, those are your older siblings."

"I continued living off the land and raising hounds while I cared for my mom. I saved enough money to buy some property which is now known as the Dusty Trail, and I still own this land. Leon, your mother kept having kids at a steady rate. You were the sixth child born in seven years. When Mutt's baby turned four, he contracted polio, which was a contagious and devastating disease few people survived before the vaccination became available. Mutt and Pearl did everything in their power to help save that boy, but their lovely blond child died, leaving them grief-stricken for years. During the time the boy was being cared for, the common practice to eliminate the spread of polio was a major concern so Mutt and I had to burn and bury every piece of clothing that child wore. We also burned every other contagious article the boy had come in contact with. I suggested to Mutt we burn and bury those items right here where we sit. Mutt and I oftentimes have come back here to talk about anything from sports to heavier topics such as life's problems. This area was our sanctuary that allowed us privacy to talk, laugh or sometimes cry over the pressures of life. This old oak has certainly heard some wild stories over the years."

"Leon, after you were born, my mother passed away from liver cancer, which was a terrible and painful way to die. I was so relieved when she passed on to a better place. Her death really threw me for a loop. With support from our friends and family, I became determined to help anyone who needed and deserved it. After my mom passed, Mutt's mom also got very ill. Pearl and Mutt moved right into her home to care for her. Pearl was surely a gem, caring for Mutt's mom day and night. Mutt would oftentimes come down here alone to collect his thoughts and pray for answers to life's problems. I knew he also wanted to be close to his son's articles we had burned. For some reason, that gave him a sense of peace, or perhaps a connection to the boy. I also made regular trips to this oak to pray for strength and courage. One might say this huge old oak is representative of our family's temple. Now that I think about it, this spot has always been a place the three of us have gravitated to when troubled."

"One cold afternoon while I was splitting wood, I was surprised to see Mutt walking into the shed looking extremely tired and exhausted, with tears running down his face. I quickly put down my axe. I walked toward him expecting the worst, and when I got close he crumbled into my arms. I knew his mom had probably passed away during the night. I wasn't heartless, but Mutt's behavior was more dramatic than I expected. I tried to console him the only way I knew how, but he kept insisting on coming to our special place under this oak. That display of grief and anger shocked the hell out of me, because Mutt had confided in me that he often selfishly wished his mom would pass away peacefully in her sleep. I thought he seemed prepared for accepting the inevitable. The two of us walked toward this oak with Mutt's old redbone that had followed his master in distress. When we arrived, it was here where we now sit together, Mutt threw a fit, yelling and crying out in pain. Christ, that scared the living hell out of me! Mutt was totally out of control of his emotions, so I watched accepting his display of grief, knowing there was absolutely nothing I could do. I was forced to watch in disbelief. After some time, Mutt slowly regained some composure. His redbone hound was so perplexed and confused he hid behind this boulder. I had seen trauma surrounding death before, but nothing that compared to that display by my good friend."

"With tears flowing, he sat down next to me, shaking uncontrollably, so I put my arm around his shoulders hoping to comfort him. To my surprise, he stood up briskly, telling me crazy stupid things that from my perspective, sounded ridiculous. Mutt finally calmed down from sheer exhaustion but continued walking in circles. Then his hound got up and walked toward his master, which helped comfort my loyal, loving friend. That hound did the trick and finally Mutt took a seat next to me. He frantically said, 'Lee we need to talk.' That was very obvious from my friend's vivid performance. I waited anxiously for him to calm down and gain more composure. Then he slowly started to explain his erratic behavior."

"He started out very slowly. Apparently, early that evening, Mutt's mom had called Pearl and Mutt to her bedside, telling them she knew it was her time to go. He said she seemed stronger than ever, but they stayed at her side, taking a seat next to her bed. She said she needed to confess a sin she had carried with her for over fifty-five years and realized if she didn't, she wasn't going to be received into heaven. Pearl and Mutt listened intently while she gave her confession. Apparently, during the year before she married her husband, she and my dad periodically dated as friends, but one evening at a barn dance they drank homemade wine and had more than they should have. Things quickly got out of control and that evening she and my dad had a sexual encounter that resulted in serious trouble a month later. Mutt's mom had attracted the man she had pursued, so she tricked him into thinking he was the father of the child she was carrying. He didn't know the difference and she said she never divulged the truth to anyone. Mutt's mom had carried that secret inside for all those years. What a burden to carry! Mutt was my half-brother. Yes, Leon its true. Mutt was your half-uncle and Ray's great-half-uncle is the only way I know how to explain your connection. Does this information help explain some of your questions regarding my apparent inability to think clearly?"

My dad was speechless again, but I needed and wanted to hear more, so I simply asked a question that seemed obvious even to me. Does this mean Mutt was really my uncle?" I was stupid for not really understanding the consequences of that question. I got up, looking around for more firewood. I had a habit of always needing to be busy when I felt stressed or anxious. I was serious and looking for words. After putting more wood on the fire, I knelt next to uncle and he was shaking his head in disbelief, so I offered another question I felt needed explanation. I asked why that secret was never disclosed before. Uncle realized the significance of my question and patted my head saying, "Sit down, Ray, I have more to explain." Dad was somberly digesting this revelation, so he meekly kept seated alongside uncle. The hounds were next to me giving me some badly needed comfort. Uncle started poking at the fire. Sparks from the fire were drifting into the darkness, which always reminded me of stars dancing into heaven. With a very low, grim voice, uncle continued. "After laying Mutt's mom to rest, uncle and Mutt set up a meeting to discuss the difficult reality and how that situation should be handled going forward into the future. They met once again down here under the oak and started discussing the very complicated repercussions that revelation could create. There were several innocent people to consider, along with the consequence of possibly tearing families apart." Uncle went on saying the reputations of their parents and families were at stake, so uncle and his half-brother decided to deal with that reality on their own. They would keep it to themselves, except that Pearl obviously knew, and she allowed them to make the decision on their own."

Dad interrupted uncle, asking what all this had to do with him. That's when my uncle leaned back to stretch, indicating the answer was ready to be disclosed. He told Dad, who had stood up at this point, to sit down and prepare himself for information he might not believe. He also asked Dad to try and keep an open mind. Every nerve in my body was shaking as I was wondering what would flow out of uncle's mouth next. I was very young, but I was empathetic. I understood the obvious pain these circumstances created for uncle and Mutt.

What could possibly be coming next? Uncle Lee stood, asking Dad for the three of us to sit close together because he felt a need to be closer allowing us to hold hands in unity. Sitting, we held hands in a circle of security. That weird request was honored out of respect. Suddenly, our hounds started acting strange. They both walked around nervously and Dad noticed, but he remained seated and silent. Uncle again started to speak and told dad that the other day I had been down here looking and seeking answers that involved the heavy emotions Mutt's death had caused. He went on saying, "Leon, your son and I have a serious confession to make, but remember this may be difficult to accept."

Dad looked up over the boulder and strangely enough seemed very serene. My dad's mood change caused my uncle and I to look in that direction and there he was. It was the older gent wearing a hunting jacket with that cap tipped back and wearing black packs. He stood leaning on his cane for support; however, he appeared calm and very confident giving off a sense of peace and serenity just like he had the other day. The three of us were mesmerized and our hounds started walking slowly toward this stranger. He knelt down, patted them both and with a pleasant smile on his face quickly turned his head and looked behind him. He slowly shifted his cane into his left hand and reached out his right hand appearing to welcome someone special. The three of us were motionless as we were captivated on this moment of truth. I heard my uncle gasp for air and suddenly the moon seemed brighter, illuminating the man, along with another male walking in his direction. When the other man appeared closer, they met, put out their hands shook and then hugged with apparent happiness. A cloud quickly covered the moon and the light was gone and so were both male images. No one moved a muscle for what felt like a lifetime. It was finally Dad who spoke first, by asking uncle, "Who in the hell are those two men and what in the hell just happened?"

"Well, to answer your first question, the man with the cane is my father and the other man who appeared was the man Mutt grew up thinking was his natural dad. What we just witnessed is debatable, so I cannot honestly answer that question," he said.

The three of us were shocked and confused by this dramatic and vivid vision which couldn't be denied. Dad made several attempts to start a normal conversation, but fell short. Our emotions were running rampant. I recall that any attempt to regain strength after our experience seemed fruitless. We were not in denial; we were probably just a bit traumatized and maybe a little weak in the knees! After witnessing that vision, I would have to say that our reactions were typical and should have been expected.

My uncle finally broke the silence by saying, "Leon, I think maybe now you probably understand why these past few days have left me struggling in my attempt to regain composure regarding Mutt's death. I also hope this explains Ray's relentless search for meaning and truth. All of us have been dealing with circumstances that unfortunately, can be perceived as over-reacting. First of all, Mutt's death has prompted me to disclose some painful secrets I had hoped would remain buried forever. I was confronted by Ethel, Martha and you, who inadvertently forced me to divulge those secrets. I had no choice. I knew the revelations would cause pain for the innocent people affected. It's not easy protecting your loved ones from the painful truth. I felt responsible and I needed to explain some of these issues to Ray without destroying his unconditional faith in our relationship, which I hold so dear."

"Ray simply wandered down here as we both have numerous times ourselves over the years. He confessed to me how he felt while talking about Mutt's funeral and what he had unfortunately and innocently encountered while standing under this significant old oak. Unfortunately, he witnessed a vision of my dad which he certainly wasn't prepared to handle. He didn't know who or what he was seeing. When he initially told me of his vision, I found I wasn't prepared for his confession and I failed to react appropriately. After thinking about his experience, I realized the reasons for his confusion because I had personally seen that same vision down here myself. In fact, I had witnessed the same vision three other times in my life, so I knew he was telling the truth. I felt guilty because he was being confronted with so many serious questions he deserved answers for. I suddenly became mindful of the fact that he needed me for guidance. I was scared, yet I felt accountable for his confusion. I understood I was perhaps the only person who could provide the answers to ease his fears and resolve his insecurities. At that time I didn't have the energy, capability or insight to verbalize the complications of what he had witnessed. So, it happens to be perfect timing that you decided to walk down the Dusty Trail searching for the two of us. You were obviously concerned for our safety and welfare. Your presence also made it possible for you to witness the gift of this amazing spiritual experience firsthand. It certainly makes Ray's life easier not having to carry this observation all alone. He now has both of us to share it with."

Uncle was humble as he continued, "At my age, it's typical for people to think I have perhaps gone slightly over the edge, and at Ray's young age, everybody would probably just think it was only a bad dream or nightmare. Having you witness this vision with us gives Ray and I serious credibility, which offers relief from any speculation that we were both perhaps imagining this spiritual experience. You're the rock that gives our vision believability."

With a sense of concern, uncle finally said, "It's getting close to suppertime and Ethel will be worried, so let's put out the fire. I think the three of us need to decide how to handle this matter as we walk home." Then uncle said, "Perhaps it would be even better if we all sleep on this experience and discuss the situation after we've had some food and badly needed rest."

Dad simply said, "Uncle, you're right. There's just no way to put this emotional experience to bed tonight on top of dealing with Mutt's funeral. Trying to put everything in proper perspective isn't immediately possible or necessary. I just want to take time to sincerely apologize to the two of you for creating total confusion without thinking. I'm very sorry I selfishly jumped to conclusions. I should have known better."

Uncle replied, "I think your reaction was normal under the circumstances." Standing alongside my dad and uncle, I was aware that each of them had an arm around my shoulders and I understood that this experience was about unity, compassion and most importantly, love. Thankfully, we were each back on the same page before turning toward another chapter that will hopefully clear up some unresolved issues.

Finally, my uncle relieved some tension and told Dad he could keep the gold pocket watch for good luck and we all laughed. Uncle's humor under pressure was a great way to put things into perspective while he apologized to my father with a simple, yet symbolic acceptance of forgiveness. The hounds walked ahead as normal, leading us home. Dad was walking behind me while uncle slowly followed all of us, which showed he was firmly behind the family as usual.

After leashing the hounds, uncle walked toward his home alone. He was quiet. I assumed he was probably filled with serious thoughts and feelings swirling in his head and heart once again. Mom met Dad on the porch looking sad, but relieved to see us. She asked Dad where uncle was and after Dad informed her he had gone home, she shook her head and simply walked off the porch toward uncle's small, yet significant refuge. Dad and I casually walked into the kitchen, removed our heavy clothes and stood next to the wood stove warming up. Sis was totally oblivious to what was going on and seemed content playing with her paper dolls. Several minutes later, hearing footsteps on the porch, Dad looked in that direction. Mom and uncle walked into the kitchen. They each carried a bundle of clothes, along with uncle's comfortable bed pillow. Mom was perceptive. She was obviously aware of Uncle's acute loneliness and had convinced him there was no need for him to eat or spend the night alone. She had suggested my uncle sleep on the couch, close to his loved ones. Uncle, in his typical display of gratitude, softly asked, "What's for supper?"

Mom's reply opened the door to lighten up the mood when she responded, "Venison and potatoes with mushroom gravy."

Dad simply said, "We'll get the Grey Ghost during the evening watch tomorrow!"

CHAPTER 27

Slowly Walking into Recovery

During supper that evening, our conversation seemed awkward. There were so many topics we had to avoid that the subject matter was kept light. Uncle seemed to be picking at his food. I assumed he was deep in thought trying to get a handle on the complications of the day's events. Dad and Mom were quiet and polite. Cindy wasn't aware of all the problems the family had encountered, so she asked an inappropriate question that floored my mom and dad. She said, "Where's Martha, and why did she leave in such a rush this afternoon?" The question was innocent, yet my parents shifted uncomfortably in their seats. Dad tried to change the subject while uncle just continued to pick at his supper. My uncle lifted his head and looked toward mom nodding ever so slightly indicating he didn't mind Cindy's question. It was obvious that he expected mom to answer.

Mom was nervous and understood she had been placed in a very tough spot, so she simply said, "I'm sorry, Cindy, but I honestly don't know where she went for certain."

Uncle Lee looked over his glasses before bravely asking Mom how Martha reacted to his disclosure about Walking Charlie. Mom was cornered, realizing the need to reveal the truth as she understood it. With everyone staring at mom waiting for her to answer, she said Martha's reaction wasn't what she had expected. Martha had thrown a fit after Dad left the shed. She accused uncle of being demented and went on to say that he was trying to sabotage her father's reputation out of jealousy and spite. Mom really shocked Dad and especially uncle, when she said that Martha indicated that the only reason uncle made up the story about Charlie was because uncle was mean, cruel and going off his rocker. She continued saying that uncle was always envious and jealous of her family's success and prosperity. With that information out and in the open, uncle just sat there transfixed, yet he seemed to be smiling. I thought he also appeared slightly agitated, but a few moments later I could see that he almost appeared relieved.

Taking another hot roll and asking for the butter, he simply responded with a serious and enlightening statement. "Cindy, Martha is a very nice lady when everything goes her way, but things became very complicated today. Martha, as usual, avoided the difficult truth because she never possessed the ability to accept life on life's terms. That has never really been part of her personality. She has proven to be capable of dealing with other people's issues and problems, but unfortunately, she has a history of running away from her own personal problems." Uncle went on, saying, "It's very sad, but it appears that Martha has once again run from the truth like she has time and time again. Obviously, she wants nothing to do with her half-brother. As far as I'm concerned, this is the very last time that she'll ever pull this crap on me and my family. Her inference that I was lying really doesn't surprise me."

Uncle saw that my sister was completely confused by his explanation, so he tried again. He gave another explanation in simpler terms that Sis could perhaps comprehend easier. Then uncle stood, grim-faced, saying, "Martha is no longer welcomed by me or this immediate family unless someone feels the need to contact her for their selfish, narrow-minded needs. If that happens in the future, I will be very angry and disappointed."

My sister was still for the first time I could remember. Finally, she spoke up, "Well, that's all right with me, because I really didn't like her very much anyway. Martha always told me how poor we all were not being able to have nice new clothes and she said we lived in a run-down old house. I like it here in this house next to you, uncle, and I think my clothes are fine and always clean and fresh."

Uncle replied, "You're absolutely right, Cindy. Always remember how important it is to love and be loved in return."

Cindy simply said, "I know one thing for sure. We all love each other and it makes me feel happy."

Uncle smiled at Sis, reaching out for her small hand. With his wrinkled hand wrapped around hers, he said directly to her, "Regardless of what happens in the future, always remember that everyone sitting around this table tonight will always love and protect you to the best of our ability." Then he laughed, adding, "And that also includes Freckles and that old redbone," which made my sister giggle endlessly. Cindy's laughter was infectious and we all laughed as we watched her. It was hard not to notice her cute freckled face accentuated by her new braids with ribbons.

With supper complete, my sister asked for dessert as usual. My sis always had a sweet tooth. Mom smiled and reached into her apron pocket, pulling out a handful of butterscotch candy she had confiscated from Mutt's funeral. Uncle unwrapped his butterscotch candy and said, "This dessert represents Mutt's help from above, putting this day behind us. I really hope this gives everyone the courage and strength to move forward with renewed optimism."

Later that evening, with Sis and I tucked into bed, my thoughts drifted from the funeral to the vision and it felt like a dream. I recall wishing it had been just a nightmare, but I knew better. I wondered why people complicated everything from the simple task of going to bed to just helping friends when they were sad or lonely. For that matter, I suddenly realized that uncle was right again. "The truth always sets you free." His quote accepting life on life's terms radiated throughout my tired body as I pulled the warm blankets up under my chin and fell sound asleep.

It was suddenly Sunday morning and the sun was shining in the window. Sis was up and moving about, which indicated I had overslept. I looked out the window after I heard uncle's door slam. The sun looked warm and inviting, but there was heavy frost on uncle's Nash, so it had to be cold in spite of the sunny day. Uncle had walked over to start a fire in the wood stove which had not been attended to for several hours. I could hear Mom and Dad downstairs talking without uncle being around. I overheard Dad say that his vacation really started off badly but he hoped things would get better today. Mom replied, "You really need to spend some quiet time with Ray and Uncle Lee. Why don't the three of you go check traps and look around for evidence of the Grey Ghost?"

I knew her comment was out of concern after dealing with the entire set of circumstances that had transpired yesterday. Her suggestion was accepted by Dad with some relief. After putting my black sneakers on, I walked downstairs, where I was warmly greeted by Dad. He told me to eat and get dressed because we were headed for Clayton's after breakfast. I was happy with that decision. While I was eating breakfast, Uncle Lee walked into the kitchen wearing his hunting outfit ,apparently all ready to go. This opportunity offered Dad and me the chance to take a badly needed rest from the problems that had surfaced yesterday afternoon. Uncle looked refreshed, as if a heavy burden had been lifted from his shoulders. That was exactly what had happened last night, which was an indication he was slowly accepting the changes in his life.

Mom and Sis were busy getting ready for church. I overheard Dad say that we would drop them off. They would most likely get a ride home from one of my aunts or uncles. With it being hunting season, I realized my uncles were probably in the woods, so it would probably be an aunt they hitched a ride from.

With everyone ready except Sis, Mom yelled for her to hurry, and when she walked down the stairs she was wearing a hunting cap that had appeared out of nowhere. Uncle laughed uncontrollably, asking her where the cap came from. Sis replied, "I found it on my bed this morning." The entire family stood there in disbelief. Dad took the cap, explaining he had found it yesterday walking down the Dusty Trail and had put it in his pocket, but had forgotten he had it. Then he also revealed the cap he found was old and battered, but this cap appeared fairly new. Sis laughed and confessed that she hadn't really found the cap on her bed. She said she saw the cap in Dad's jacket and had decided to wear it out of respect for Mutt. Needless to say the adults were relieved since they certainly weren't prepared for another mystery. My father wasn't completely convinced with my sister's explanation, but he let it slide.

We all jumped into uncle's Nash and headed for church to drop off Sis and Mom. Sis was given permission to wear her cap and uncle softly said as he watched Mom and Cindy walk together into the church, "Cindy is certainly a cute little girl. It's hard to resist her charm and confidence."

Dad offered, "That's all right for now." I found myself wondering how her cuteness would cause Dad future problems as she got older.

My uncle laughed and replied, "Hold on to your hat! Cindy likes hunting caps."

While driving toward Clayton's, the conversation was general, with no reference to yesterday's events. What a relief! We all needed time to regroup and catch up on some well-deserved rest from the drama Mutt's passing had caused. There was no need to beat a dead horse during this particular time. Reaching Clayton's, we unlocked the gate and immediately noticed Clayton driving his tractor and heading toward the beaver pond. Dad honked his horn to get his attention. Clayton stopped and acknowledged us by waving energetically. Clayton was a kind man and a very hard worker. Dad said that Clayton loved his farm and enjoyed his life by doing what he loved. Uncle said Clayton was born a farmer and he never deviated from his calling. I remember thinking how nice it must be to be living on a farm and doing what you love every single day. That seemed to be a very simple concept, but I believed it at the time and even more so today.

Clayton informed uncle that his farm hand had checked our traps that morning and the animals were skinned and drying in his barn. That friend of uncle's had taken the liberty of helping, realizing there was a possibility that our family wouldn't be able to take care of the trap line any time soon. Then, out of the blue, uncle asked Clayton for a huge favor. Uncle wanted to know if Clayton could move his wagons and surprisingly, asked if he could borrow around sixteen bales of hay. Clayton was receptive, but asked two questions that both Dad and I would have asked if he hadn't beat us to it. Uncle told Clayton his plan pertained to the Grey Ghost and that we would follow him to help him relocate the wagons and also help get the bales.

Driving behind the tractor, my dad asked what uncle had up his sleeve in an effort to better understand the game plan.

Uncle simply said, "You'll agree with this move after we get everything organized." It was so typical of uncle to keep his ideas to himself for as long as possible. That characteristic wasn't for the purpose of being controlling. Uncle simply liked to keep us guessing, which always created more intrigue and mystery.

Reaching the beaver pond, we stopped to explain where uncle wanted the wagons located. He walked to the end of the hedgerow and showed Clayton where to place the first wagon. Then he walked seventy-five yards further down the harvested cornfield to a location just off the field. This area provided the capability of seeing into the swamp around thirty yards at best. Dad walked slowly down toward the swamp, looking around. I happened to be in the best location, sitting on Clayton's tractor between his legs. I had never been on a tractor before, so I was really enjoying this experience. Regardless of the results, it was evident the four of us were enjoying the peace and stillness that accompanied this beaver pond and huge swamp. After getting the wagons located, we all headed back to get the hay bales. A smaller wagon was hauled out of a barn and loaded quickly. Uncle seemed pleased with himself, and that pleased Dad. Sitting on the small wagon with Dad, we enjoyed our unexpected hay ride. Life seemed normal once again!

CHAPTER 28

Grey Ghost: His Strength May be his Weakness

Once the hay bales were dropped off by Clayton, we placed ten bales on the wagon closest to the end of the hedgerow and the other six were positioned on the wagon nearest the swamp. The wagons were located about a hundred yards apart and a small blind was built on each wagon, similar to a duck blind. Two additional bales were used as seats.

Uncle Lee asked me to run to the Nash and get the old blanket that Freckles always laid on when he was being transported for training or special hunting events. Behind the blind on the wagon closest to the swamp, uncle wrapped Freckles' blanket around the bail to be used as a seat. Then uncle reached into his jacket pocket and removed some Yankee Girl chew. I figured he needed a chew himself but he certainly fooled me and surprisingly pushed that small plug between two bails. The wind was blowing the scent of Yankee Girl chew right into the swamp.

Uncle continued rearranging the bales and I noticed that Dad was having problems controlling his curiosity. I could see that he wanted to share his opinion. I could also sense a little confusion on his part; yet he understood from past experience with uncle that he would be given his chance to speak in good time. I must admit that I was also somewhat baffled with the concept that was transpiring before my eyes. Uncle was emphatic about this meticulous preparation. He carefully attended to each detail with precision, and it almost felt as if he was ignoring us. With the blinds built to his satisfaction, he nodded with some relief and it was obvious that he was pleased with his work. He finally took a seat on the wagon. While resting, he started explaining his entire plan in detail. Dad was interested and started jiggling the change in his pants pocket. He was confused. I knew he was wondering about the need for the blanket or chew. It seemed obvious that this maneuver by my uncle was quite strange.

As uncle sat there smiling with a sense of accomplishment, he informed Dad and myself that he had given some serious thought to my theory. I had always believed that the Grey Ghost knew where danger lurked by smell and sight. Uncle said, "This wagon was a decoy where my dad would sit during the watch." He added, "I'm sorry, Leon, your chances aren't real good, but this will work if you agree." Dad was all ears, with some reservation showing. I wanted to figure out the next move, so I asked what needed to be done. Uncle got off the wagon with Dad's help and said, "Remember, his strength may also be his weakness." My uncle seemed confident with his plan, so Dad went along out of respect. He also understood that this process had been thought out down to every single minor detail. While the three of us walked back to the first wagon, we openly discussed what was needed to complete his idea. As we approached the last wagon located at the top of the hedgerow, he pulled out a small bottle of fox urine and poured some on each tire. Apparently, fox urine was being used as a cover scent, plus uncle said he felt deer investigated fox markings out of curiosity. Then to my surprise, uncle asked me to walk along side the hedgerow while he sat behind the blind watching intently. I walked slowly and did what I was asked and quickly returned waiting for further instruction. After thinking for a short time, uncle asked Dad to get the heavy brush clippers out of the trunk. When Dad returned, the three of us walked to a location in the hedgerow and uncle started cutting a shooting lane approximately four feet wide. He told Dad, "This is where it all ends for that old bastard."

Dad laughed, saying, "Please explain how this is going to work."

Uncle affectionately rustled my hair, saying, "Okay, let's go sit on the wagon with the blanket and chew while I explain the process. It's all right if we leave human scent on that wagon, because it might help." On our walk, uncle's explanation regarding sight and smell indicated my observations on the Dusty Trail were entwined with this well-thought-out attempt. Uncle said he had given my "nose ability" serious thought and found my observations informative. He felt my deer-watching behavior, along with other significant details I had witnessed down the Dusty Trail, were very interesting. He also said it had made him think outside the box. As a result, he thought my observations had merit and gave them serious thought. Our conversation had motivated uncle, so he decided to devise a plan that incorporated my ability to smell deer and take advantage of my power. Based on that premise, he continued to say, "I felt the Grey Ghost's strengths were going to become his weakness." I was so pleased, along with Dad, recognizing that uncle had kept an open mind and for once listened to me. My uncle went on saying the Ghost would need at least five days to get used to the wagons with blinds. The Grey Ghost was very smart, but uncle felt the odors on the decoy wagon would confuse him. Our work could cause the ghost to make a mistake, directing him further down toward the hedgerow wagon. Then out of the blue, uncle said he felt the Grey Ghost had a habit of working his way along the hedgerow to the cornfield to feed after hunters left the area on their morning watch. He went on explaining how he remembered the ghost had been spotted between ten and eleven o'clock on three occasions by accident and he felt the next time should be his demise. This plan might take a few days requiring patience, but he felt it was well worth the effort. Then he asked Dad and myself what we thought about his plan.

Dad realized even if he didn't completely agree or understand, this was certainly not the time to divulge any negative opinion even if he had one. I, on the other hand, had another idea and I spoke up and said so. I am sure it sent a shiver up Dad's spine not knowing what I was going to ask. I said, "There is no reason for anyone to sit on the decoy wagon." I continued saying, "Dad should be placed to the right side of the hedgerow wagon down toward the end of the swamp." I also offered that Dad should sit where he always liked to watch. Uncle was all ears and asked how I knew where dad watched. Dad responded that he had shown me that area the other day while we were checking traps. I suggested that perhaps with Dad in that location, it would help funnel the Ghost in our direction, but if it didn't, perhaps Dad could get a shot if the Ghost were to continue working his way in his direction. I also took the opportunity to remind uncle the Grey Ghost was very unpredictable.

My uncle said, "Ray, that makes sense. We'll do it your way because your nose is the ultimate answer anyway!"

Dad finally offered his opinion suggesting the decoy wagon would also divert the does or other deer up the hedgerow, which would also give the Ghost a false sense of security. Dad went on to say that he thought the entire plan could work even better if he were to walk up further than the decoy wagon and leave cigarette butts along another runway that he noticed during his walk. Dad suggested that it might help divert and make the deer avoid taking that route to the cornfield. Uncle agreed and told him now would be as good a time as ever to put this plan in place. He told dad to get the cigarette butts from the ash tray in the Nash and place them accordingly. Dad smiled like a little boy getting approval as he walked to perform his task.

Needless to say, we were filled with excitement and renewed motivation, which was badly needed since we were now an important part of uncle's enthusiastic plan. We were a team! After Dad returned after placing his cigarette butts where he wanted, we drove to pick up our fur and thanked Clayton and his farm hand who had helped uncle keep our trap line going. My father calmly suggested we leave shortly because he was concerned that uncle was getting tired and required a rest and perhaps a well-deserved lunch. After some brief conversation with uncle's friends regarding Mutt's death, the three of us got into the Nash and headed toward home. This had been an enjoyable morning, putting us in a relaxed mood. Uncle said, "Now everything would be perfect if it would snow, covering up our tracks or any other evidence we may have left behind." The ride home contained little conversation because everyone seemed engrossed in their own thoughts.

On the way back, Dad caught both uncle and me by surprise by pulling into the doctor's office that was located near the hospital. Uncle didn't hold back, "What in the hell are we doing here?"

Dad mildly shrugged his shoulders, explaining, "This might be the perfect time for you to have that follow-up appointment. Perhaps the doc is available to give you a quick examination. Our family has used this doctor for years. I would have to say that with over seventy-five patients from our family alone, I believe he'll give us some degree of priority." The plan worked to perfection because we happened to catch the doctor outside walking toward his vehicle. The doctor greeted us warmly and Dad casually asked him to do us a favor and check uncle over. The doc agreed, but seemed a bit concerned, suggesting that uncle needed five or six days of home rest before he got exhausted again. Otherwise, something very serious could happen. At first, my uncle rejected his suggestion, but then he looked at me and saw my grave concern, so he accepted the doc's advise. Uncle admitted, "I am a bit tired after this week's turmoil. Perhaps you're right for the first time since I've known you, doc!" Both uncle and the doctor laughed at my uncle's attempt at dry humor, which was always present yet never anticipated.

The doctor quickly responded without missing a beat, "If you take my advice, it will be the first time!"

They laughed, shook hands and uncle said, "Thank you, doc, you're all right."

Later, while entering our drive, uncle seemed quiet and preoccupied. It must have been significant because I could see he was troubled and something was bothering him. Dad simply said, "Uncle, don't worry about the store. The family has you covered."

Uncle responded, "You're always trying to keep a step ahead of me, and this time it worked perfectly. Thank you both for being there for me when I need it."

Dad seemed pleased by his show of humility and thanks. Dad's response was short, but significant. He simply said, "You've been there for us for over forty years, so it's the least we can do." I was very concerned for uncle's health, but Dad's display of love and gratitude overflowed with respect and unconditional love.

As dad parked the car, Cindy flew out of the house without her coat. She greeted us with the news that Pearl was inside visiting with Mom and lunch was being prepared. My mother had anticipated well, which showed she recognized Dad's behavior better then he realized. I could see that uncle seemed concerned by Pearl's visit, but said nothing. Walking slowly inside our kitchen, I noticed Pearl making herself at home helping Mom. She looked weary and tired, just like uncle, but she forced a smile as we entered. Uncle removed his cap walking toward her and put out his arms. She hesitated briefly, but walked into them for comfort, which they both needed. Their display of vulnerability was obvious because of their need to handle their grief with openness and honesty. No tears were evident, yet you could cut the emotions with a knife. My parents stood by quietly allowing Pearl and uncle to gain badly needed strength from each other. After all, they had been an intricate part of each other's life's and for over fifty years. With the display of acceptance and with their grief slowly subsiding, Mom lightened the mood by suggesting we sit down and have lunch. She had prepared rabbit soup with noodles, along with grouse sandwiches, which was very typical for Sunday lunch. The kitchen was small, but the atmosphere was filled with the love and kindness that was always prevalent around the small table, now set with Mom's best dishes.

While eating, the conversation was delicate; however, it was more relaxed than I expected. Pearl seemed comfortable while she thanked our family for our support. She went on saying she had expected the worst, but wasn't really prepared for Mutt's passing, even though she knew it could be coming at any time. She also indicated Mutt was prepared, having given her orders to give his traps and rifle to me! Pearl said Mutt wanted to give me a leg up on uncle and Dad! The adults laughed, but in reality understood the significance of his request. Pearl stopped for a few seconds and continued after regaining her composure. She asked permission to ask a very serious question and uncle replied, "Ask anything you feel the need to ask."

So she asked, "Does Ethel know about Mutt's attachment to this family?"

Uncle simply said, "Not completely." He went on looking at Mom, saying, "Ethel, yesterday afternoon when you, Martha and your husband approached me in the shed I couldn't divulge the entire truth about Mutt because Martha started throwing a fit about Charlie. I had to leave because realized she's history and I didn't want her to know any more than necessary."

Mom had a serious look on her face and injected, "What am I missing?"

"Ethel," he said, "This information has never been shared with anyone, including your husband, until yesterday." He went on, explaining that Mutt was his half-brother but the only people who were aware of this were Pearl, Mutt and himself. "That reality has been a secret buried deep in our family for over forty years. I disclosed this information to Ray and your husband yesterday afternoon while we were under the oak down the Dusty Trail. I will explain everything later, but please don't feel you've been kept out of the loop about this situation. I guess we have to decide if there is a need to bring this issue to anyone else or just keep it among ourselves. Does anyone have a strong feeling either way?"

My mother slowly reached out her hand to Pearl, saying, "Welcome to our family, Pearl." She elaborated a bit further saying somehow she wondered because she always felt that Uncle's and Mutt's friendship seemed to be so strong and based on more than just friendship. "To be honest, it's a blessing in disguise, because Pearl needs this family for support during this very difficult time. Keeping that hidden and locked inside for all these years must have been a heavy burden for the three of you to carry. That also explains why this family was such a significant part of Mutt's wake and funeral. It's very sad, but I know deep down in my heart your decision was made at the time based on the heartbreak sharing this information would have caused. I've never questioned your honesty or values, so please understand that I stand behind any decision you, Pearl and my husband make."

Apparently, at some point my sister had gotten bored with the conversation and went upstairs. Before we knew it she appeared back in the kitchen and was wearing that old hunting cap cocked on the side of her head. When Pearl spotted that cap her eyes opened wide and she asked Cindy where she had gotten it. Dad explained how he had found it on the Dusty Trail yesterday. Pearl looked down sadly and then stood up and walked to Sis and removed the cap tenderly. She gently looked inside under the tag and with a gasp said, "I cannot believe it. This is the exact cap I bought for Mutt two months ago. I looked everywhere for this cap this morning." Pearl sat down very slowly. I swear you could hear a pin drop with the speculation swirling in the minds of everyone in our kitchen.

With confusion evident on everyone's face, uncle said, "There must be some mistake. Let's not speculate any further."

Dad swiftly changed the subject by informing Mom and Pearl about uncle's visit with the doctor that afternoon. He mentioned the need for uncle to get some rest and that the family would need to cover the store for the next five days. He said he could open up in the morning, but needed help in the evenings. Mom said, "That shouldn't be a problem. I'm sure one of your brothers can close up." Pearl was listening to the conversation and digesting the information being discussed. She seemed to have something she wanted to say. Finally, she spoke up and said that it had been extremely difficult to adjust to being alone at home since Mutt's passing. She said she had been giving some serious thought to getting a job, because she figured working may help pass the time. Perhaps getting out and talking to people could help get her mind off of her loneliness and sadness. Plus, she could also use some extra money.

Uncle asked, "What hours would be best for you, Pearl?"

She replied, "Mornings and afternoons would be most suitable."

He reached across the table for her hand, saying, "You've got yourself a deal." She smiled graciously. Uncle also smiled with some relief, saying, "That works out great because this arrangement allows us the opportunity to hunt during the day and someone can cover the evenings for the next week. I expect to be back to normal by Saturday, so it appears this issue is resolved." Then he looked at Pearl and said, "Are you sure you are ready to assume work so soon under the circumstances?"

Pearl smiled and said, "Yes. I really need to keep busy and doing this will also help you and your family. It's a perfect situation for all of us."

Hearing that comment, Dad replied, "Pearl, this is also your family now. Always remember that from this day forward." So it appeared one issue would be handled giving the adults some peace of mind-at least regarding coverage of the store.

Uncle seemed tired, but went next door to get the extra set of keys handing them to Pearl. She also appeared weary when she said, "It's getting somewhat late. I should get home and try to get some rest. It's hasn't been easy adjusting to Mutt not being around in the evening."

My sister was playing with her doll and she innocently blurted out, "It feels like something's missing today," bringing the reality of the situation back to the forefront.

Dad stood up and put on his jacket as he prepared to give Pearl a ride home. After the typical goodbyes, Pearl and my father left. Perhaps things were slowly starting to return back to some semblance of normality. After Dad left, I put on my warm clothes and walked with uncle over to his home expecting to help carry wood in from the shed. He needed to start fires in the stove in his kitchen, along with the stove in the trapper's shed. While uncle started the fire in the shed, I went over and for the first time took a seriously good look at all the gorgeous fur hanging on the walls drying. I must say that it was rewarding. I felt a sense of pride because I knew that I played a small role in this success. This will always be a vivid memory of mine since it was my first trapping season. I cannot say my first season was uneventful. In fact, it was filled with so many significant events. I remember hoping things would improve for everyone's sake. With the fire quickly warming up the small shed, Uncle turned around and sat down in the recliner gently admitting, "Ray, I'm really tired and need some rest." I hugged him and quietly left the shed heading for my hounds. While I played with Freckles and the redbone, a thought occurred to me. I suddenly wondered why that old redbone hound had been retired from the hunt so early. I never thought to ask that question before, but decided to ask Dad for an answer as soon as he returned home.

Suddenly, for some unexplained reason, I felt the need to release the hounds. So I did just that and I was both shocked and surprised when they walked slowly toward the shed where uncle rested. I simply followed the hounds and opened the shed's door slowly and quietly. I didn't want to wake uncle as I allowed both hounds to enter. The hounds walked toward uncle as he slept in the tan recliner and then both pets laid down at his feet. I closed the door softly, knowing I would never forget the peaceful sign of loyalty and love being displayed by those two hounds.

The weather that afternoon was gradually turning colder, with an east wind blowing that was most likely an indication of snow. With my hands in my pockets, I walked slowly down the abandoned street. My thoughts were on the events that had transpired over the past few months. Like it or not, these situations had changed my perspective about life and it's problems. I found myself thinking about how life can change in the blink of an eye. These experiences had generated extreme emotional highs and lows. I never experienced anything like that before in my young life. I recall pondering the complicated events in an attempt to digest all my internal feelings and put them into proper perspective. As I walked, it occurred to me to keep in mind what uncle always said: "It's important to accept life on life's terms." To be honest, nothing seemed to remain the same from one day to the next. That's when I actually prayed for the strength to better accept and tolerate the things I cannot change. I realized I was again relying on advice my Uncle Lee often preached to me. As I prayed, I gave thanks for my family and friends and of course, my hounds. I was grateful knowing my uncle was safe, resting with our hounds.

Even though I knew my effort to comprehend was somewhat limited due to my age and lack of experience, I continued to ponder the issues that caused problems in relationships. It appeared to me that selfishness, along with control issues, always seemed to get in the way of relationships. I could see that a lack of consideration and stubbornness also seemed to be contributing factors. Perhaps learning these lessons while I was trying to understand all the facts would someday help me regain some badly needed faith in human behavior.

As I continued walking along deep in thought, I was happy to be sidetracked as I noticed Dad driving up the street. He stopped the car and asked if I was okay. I replied, "Yes, but I've been doing a lot of thinking and I have a few questions." With that statement, my father pulled the Chevy over to the side of the street.

Reaching across the seat, he opened the passenger door and said, "Get in." Dad seemed very concerned for my well-being and asked, "What are you troubled about?" I hesitated as I looked out the window, thinking to myself that there were so many loose ends I really didn't know where to start. Dad seemed much more aware of my issues and dilemma than I realized. He said, "Just start at the beginning and don't hold back." I was still quiet, so he said, "Ray, the entire chain of events we have been through has caused our family some un-expected issues. We will all get through this with each other's care and support." Dad went on explaining that my concerns were completely normal. "Rest assured that all of these prob-lems will be resolved one way or another in good time. I real-ize these situations and events are especially difficult for you to understand and comprehend, so all I can advise you for now is to just try and relax."

Since I knew Dad was willing to listen, my first question was why the redbone had been retired so early. I could tell Dad was surprised by that question and he even said he didn't think my concerns were necessarily about the hounds, but he answered my question anyway. He said, "One afternoon, the redbone had hit the track of a badly wounded deer, causing him to chase the deer. After that experience, it was virtually impossible to use him as a foxhound because any time the red bone hit a deer track, he took it!" Hunting deer with dogs is prohibited, so uncle had to stop using him. "Your uncle liked the hound, so he kept him out of respect and loyalty, plus he gave Freckles company."

I spoke up, "So that's why uncle avoids using the red bone, but what about the vision we witnessed and what about Martha's reaction to hearing about Walking Charlie? How do you really think these factors will affect uncle in the long run?" Dad sat back and I could tell he was trying to think of a way to set my mind at ease. My father usually hesitated before answering a difficult question. I guess I made the question especially difficult this time because I had combined two complex issues together.

My dad looked up the street before saying, "Okay, first of all, let's discuss the vision we experienced. I am not entirely sure myself about that particular situation. Have you ever heard about visions in Sunday school?"

I answered, "Yes, but I never thought about it much."

Dad went on, "Well Ray, I think the three of us have all been gifted a vision from heaven that really cannot be explained by anyone other than our maker. Does that make sense?" Without letting me answer, he went on. "Ray, since seeing that vision, I strongly believe the three of us should keep what we saw to ourselves and appreciate and accept it for what it was. I hope that helps." I nodded my head in approval. My father said, "That's great."

"Now about Martha. I know you're aware that their relationship was never great from the beginning because of the differences in their lifestyles. Uncle Lee was always his own man from a very early age, which attracted Martha to him in the first place. However, she constantly tried to change uncle's personality, along with his lifestyle. We cannot blame Martha completely because your uncle became so set in his ways that he found it very difficult to change course in the middle of the stream. They were like magnets, Ray. They always say opposites attract. But in their case, I think the risk never seemed worth the potential rewards. It really wasn't possible for either one to honestly accept each other's perspective. Time really solidified their different personalities, but as uncle always says ,you can't teach an old dog new tricks. That certainly applied to their relationship from the beginning. They often tried to meet each other halfway, but every time there seemed to be some issue that surfaced that they couldn't resolve. It drove them further apart, making it very hard to remedy their problems or correct their negative reactions. The older they got ,the more entrenched they became in their respective lifestyles and beliefs. Ray, remember one thing. Beauty is only skin deep. Martha is a fine lady, but her money and social expectations never set well with uncle. He tried, but to no one's surprise he always gravitated back to his first loves, which are his family and the outdoors. You're very young to completely understand these complex details, but as you get older you may experience a similar set of circumstances. Just remember to try and stay true to yourself. It's very important to always make an attempt to change your behavior for better without putting your fundamental emotional welfare or safety at risk. From my observation, I am afraid Martha is probably no longer going to be part of Uncle Lee's life. I personally feel this is in everyone's best interest. I'm not saying she's a bad person, but she has caused trouble in the past. They seem to have reached a point in their lives where enough is enough. Now, does that help you understand?"

I really wasn't grasping everything, but it satisfied my curiosity for the time being. I also gave Dad something else to think about when I said, "I noticed things started changing radically when Martha came onto the scene at the championship."

Dad said, "Ray, you're absolutely right, so why don't we put her completely out of the picture if that's alright with you?

I said, "Okay by me, Dad, but what about uncle?"

Dad was firm in his response, "Your uncle will never put himself in that position again, trust me. I know he's written her off forever." So with that conversation and explanation over, Dad asked where uncle was now, so I explained telling him about the hounds. Visualizing a picture of the hounds at uncle's feet, I saw my dad smile.

Pulling into our drive, Dad jumped out and unlocked and opened the trunk of the Chevy. Inside were at least ten dozen traps, along with a thirty-thirty rifle dad pulled out of a really nice gun case. On the stock of this rifle were markings indicative of Mutt's successful hunts which really pleased my father. When I reached for the rifle, he cautioned, "Be careful," when I kissed the stock. Dad was really moved by my simple gesture saying, "Let's just go inside and relax." Dad reminded me that I needed to prepare for school tomorrow. I know he was suggesting that I really needed to get structure back into my life. On that matter, I was completely in agreement. I was smart enough to be aware that returning to school would allow me the luxury of getting my thoughts away from the complications which each of us needed to handle in our own way on our own terms. With all the feelings and confusion running rampant, it seemed to me nothing was going right for anyone. It was my first serious introduction to adult problems and their approach to solving everyday issues. I was really happy that school had been enjoyable recently which helped me look forward to going back and seeing my friends.

That evening while listening to country music on the radio, my father sat relaxing with a cold beer while Mom talked on the phone to Pearl. They suddenly seemed so much closer since Mom was sensitive to Pearl's needs. Uncle was next door preparing for bed, and I couldn't help wondering how the drastic events were affecting his perspective on his future. It never occurred to me that my uncle might not recover physically. That possibility felt very threatening. Understanding I needed to think positive was evident. I was concerned about his welfare, knowing that all things in life are temporary, including life itself. Thank God it was time for bed. Saying prayers that evening was significant because I remembered uncle saying, "It's important not to get stuck in the past spinning your wheels. Sometimes you need to back up a bit to help get a head start to regain the strength to move forward." At the time he told me that, it never really registered, but it really made sense tonight.

Before my father said good night, he looked out the window toward uncle's, saying, "Ray, I hope you know that gentle, old man needs you as much as you need him. Your relationship is intertwined so tightly it appears you're a clone of uncle, only sixty years later. I never heard the word "clone" before, but at the time it felt soothing. Lying there in bed, my father also said, "Everyone is challenged with dealing with their own problems in life, so please don't feel any responsibility for the issues that have surfaced over the past few days. Always remember to try to be part of the solution, rather than part of the problem." Dad always lived by that premise and with his comfort that evening, I was able to drop off to sleep easily.

CHAPTER 29

Maybe you Can Teach an Old Dog New Tricks

After being awakened by Sis the following morning, I could smell breakfast cooking, which indicated a new day was on the horizon. It seemed as if the past few days had lasted for an eternity. Reluctantly facing the morning, I threw on a robe and slowly made my way downstairs. That particular morning I hadn't taken the time to look out the window for uncle's Nash. That oversight was very unusual and strange because checking on uncle was always my first priority every morning. My dad was relaxing on the couch sipping his coffee while listening to the local news and weather. He appeared tired or preoccupied as he simply said, "Good morning." As he picked up the local paper and opened it to the sports page, I recall him saying the only thing that ever changes in this paper are the obituaries and box scores. Mom and Sis were in the midst of a battle over Cindy's braids. Once again, my sister was angry with Mom, accusing her of tugging too hard on her hair. There was no doubt in my mind that life was working its way back to normal.

After I finished eating breakfast and dressing for school, Mom quickly reminded us, "It's very cold; you'll both need your gloves and caps." The exhaustion was evident, overtaking the atmosphere within the walls of our small home. It was obvious no one was in a particularly good mood. There was no sense of urgency and it seemed as if the family was just going through the motions. Everyone was focused on simply preparing for the cold, dreary day's responsibilities. The only noise that was radiating annoyingly throughout the house came from the radio. The morning announcer was laughing at nothing in particular, being very cheerful as usual. During his morning show called "The Coffee Hour," he always seemed overly optimistic and energized. His delivery was making me wonder if his life was really that upbeat. I asked Mom about his never-ending, almost annoying ability to be cheery every morning. She politely offered, "It's his job, Ray, but I have to admit it's over the top today." She also mentioned that she found it most irritating this morning. Dad was still bitching to himself about the weather forecast, along with having read that the Red Wings lost to the Bruins in the final minute of play.

Dad continued to muttered to himself, "Detroit always plays awful in the Boston Gardens." That news was certainly setting Dad's day off on the wrong foot.

Saying goodbye to our folks, Sis and I finally walked out onto the porch. Cindy was still upset and continued to complain about Mom. She was always miserable in the morning, so I took her hand, dragging her aggressively towards uncle's kitchen window to check and see if he was up having his coffee. He noticed us outside and waved. With that acknowledgement, we turned to start the long, cold walk to school. Both of us were looking forward to meeting our friends that we hadn't seen in five days. The rituals traditionally performed by our friends' mothers were welcomed. Arsen's mom reminded us to use the sidewalk, along with her typical warning, "Kids, remember to watch out for the cars." I found those gestures to be welcomed that morning, finally giving me a chance to smile and concentrate on something other than the continuous turbulence of the past few days.

It seemed like the school day went by quickly. I was concerned when my teacher asked me to stay after for a few extra minutes. In the past, that request usually indicated problems, but to my relief she reached into her desk searching for something. She handed me a card and said it was for my family. I realized at that point my new teacher was very kind and considerate . She said with sincerity that a death in a family is always difficult to deal with and she gently asked if everyone was okay. I responded, "It's going to be alright," and thanked her for being concerned.

She said, "Ray, situations like these are part of life's learning experiences which you cannot be taught in school."

I responded. "I know." Then, I left her classroom starting the long walk home.

The wind was blowing out of the north, making a heavy snow shower begin to start rotating. It looked just like small tornados forming in the corners of the school entryway. It was very cold, damp and miserable, and my mood mirrored the dismal, gray weather. This time of year was often drab, making everyone gripe about nothing in particular. They just complained for the sake of complaining. I remembered when the fall foliage was recently at its peak, but it was gone as fast as it had occurred and there was very little color remaining. It was sad to think that virtually nothing was left of the gorgeous natural beauty that nature had displayed just a few weeks ago.

Walking slowly alone toward home, it dawned on me that my serious conversation with my father had really helped explain some issues. I found that I was still struggling with lack of motivation and enthusiasm. Nothing felt uplifting, so I kept plugging along all by myself, sort of wishing my friends had waited for me after school. It felt strange to be walking alone without Joe, Arsen and Sam to talk to. The shortcut seemed longer than normal for some unexplained reason today. I wondered if taking the sidewalk might be quicker. Then I thought, maybe the shortcut wasn't faster after all. Perhaps it just felt that way. After all the experiences I had lately, I had become aware of the possibility that any situation could perhaps be an illusion, just like the vision. The only consistency recently was confusion propagated by situations which needed to be changed or accepted. Thank God for my hounds. They were consistent because they were always happy, tired or simply hungry.

Getting closer to home, I started running in anticipation of the warmth of the wood fire in the kitchen, but preferably the solace of the trapper's shed. Reaching home, I ran into the warm kitchen and put my books on the table. I said a quick "Hi," to Mom and ran next door to check on my uncle. Inside the garage, uncle was in the recliner napping with the hounds at his side. It was so comforting seeing one of his hands on Freckles' head and the other arm wrapped around the redbone's neck. After hearing me walk into the shed, both hounds walked toward me, waking uncle. With his glasses still sitting on his forehead and his cap tipped down on his right ear, he appeared overtired. He fought to wake up and suddenly appeared to be renewed and alert. As uncle stood up, stretching slowly, he asked how my school day had gone. That's when I noticed a radical change in his dress and appearance. He was wearing jeans with a belt, along with a nice heavy yellow sweater and turtleneck that actually matched. He was also wearing low-cut sneakers, and they were white ones at that. He looked sharp, clean shaven and I thought he appeared ten years younger. Without mentioning a word about his transition, he knew I had noticed anyway, so he simply said, "I thought it was time to make a few changes. Maybe you can teach an old dog new tricks after all."

I laughed, saying, "You look just like Dad."

He said, "Is that supposed to be a compliment?" Then he laughed and told me to sit down and warm up. "It might help if you close the door. Trust me, trying to warm up the outdoors just never seems to work." His ability to make a joke was a welcome change from his mood the past few days.

While sitting with uncle, Dad pulled into the drive. After getting out of his Chevy, I heard him walking into the garage, heading for the shed. He was wearing old hunting clothes and he greeted us by saying, "I've been sitting for four hours and the only thing I saw or heard were blue jays and some geese flying south."

Uncle laughed and said, "Some thing's never change. That's your normal hunting excuse." We all laughed while Dad sat down on the stool next to the workbench.

The conversation was light until my father took notice of uncle's new wardrobe, saying, "Christ, you've entered the 1950s. The next thing you'll be letting your hair grow long and playing a guitar.

Uncle replied, "I already know how to play a guitar, but the hair might be a problem." Uncle's delivery made my father laugh for the first time in a while. It felt wonderful seeing those two back to some semblance of their normal selves. My dad said he needed to leave the shed to clean up. He wanted to relieve Pearl early to make sure her first day at the store was all right. Uncle reminded my father that Pearl had occasionally worked in the store during the holidays. He said, "Don't worry, she's all right. I expect to be down around seven o'clock, but if there's any problem, just call." We all walked outside with a renewed feeling of getting back to our respective routines. It was great recognizing the relief displayed and shared between the three of us. The hounds stayed in the shed where it was warm and comfortable. Uncle said, "Those two dogs are a perfect match. They get along just fine."

The next two days flew by quietly without any serious problems. Dad was hunting, or at least he was going through the motions. He wasn't seeing any sign of deer to speak of, so in my infinite wisdom, I suggested he sit in the old orchard down the Dusty Trail. I reminded him about the ten-point and said if it were up to me, that's where I'd hunt. He looked at me with reluctance but said, "That might work. I could use a change of scenery anyway because I'm sick of watching and listening to the same blue jays every morning." Then he added he had been so bored that he named them Joe and Moe, making us both laugh.

Thursday evening came quickly with me waiting patiently for uncle to pick me up. I was really looking forward to join Dad and the codgers in the office area. I heard the horn and quickly said goodbye to Mom and Sis. Then I ran to join my uncle in the Nash. As I got in the car, I thought to myself that Yankee Girl sure smelled sweet, but I decided it must taste terrible. Uncle again surprised me with his neat appearance. He had on a brand-new jacket with a nice warm zip-out liner. It was bright blue, trimmed in white. Along with a red sweater and white shirt underneath, he looked quite dapper. His new jeans were pressed with nice straight seams. Uncle's rest at home was obviously working for him because he had been clean shaven for three days in a row. The transition in his appearance indicated that perhaps he decided to turn over a new leaf and make some changes in his life.

We talked about the Grey Ghost, with plans being made to execute uncle's ideas on Saturday morning. He said he would like at least six inches of new snow and it was being predicted for Friday morning. I asked if he knew any details about the wind direction expected for Friday. He simply replied, "Don't worry, Ray, we'll put your nose to good use one way or another."

Walking into the office area, the codgers immediately started giving uncle the business about his appearance, but Weasel got in the best jab by saying, "If our wives see this display, we'll never hear the end of it."

Uncle laughed, saying, "It's about time your wives stood their ground." The codgers laughed and started talking fondly about Mutt, but I noticed they avoided any negative reactions other than the reality of missing his butterscotch candy. With the dialogue concentrated on hunts, it became clear each of the codgers had filled their tags with small racks. They were more interested in providing venison and they did not appear to be interested in pursuing the Grey Ghost. My father and uncle stayed quiet and did not give them any indication of our plan.

The door to the store opened and we noticed Walking Charlie heading straight to the office area. He was wearing a nice, warm parka with matching hat and gloves. He was also wearing warm insulated packs. Charlie's face glowed with satisfaction, along with confidence, which was rare. He sat down next to uncle saying, "Lee, if it wasn't for you I really don't know what would happen to me."

My uncle smiled, saying, "Charlie, you're my friend. Don't worry because you're set up for the rest of your life. Just stay out of trouble and don't eat too much candy." Charlie got up, said good night and walked out into the cold weather with a renewed sense of purpose and warm, comfortable clothing on his back.

Leo asked uncle about Charlie's situation, so uncle explained that Charlie was a project he took on after he had been left homeless. He said, "It seemed to be the right thing to do then and it is even more meaningful now. In fact, I talked to Charlie's social worker today and I set up a small trust fund to care for the extras he deserves. I feel it's the least I can do. You see, Charlie is a victim of circumstances he cannot help, so I simply did what any one of you would have done if you were in my situation. Let's drop the subject. Just remember Charlie is special in his own way and I hope he has a long happy life with our help and his somewhat limited ability."

No one said another word. They simply got up and shook uncle's hand saying, "You're a loyal friend that we know we can depend on." They left walking together and discussing the scene they just witnessed.

During the ride home, Dad told me he was so proud of the action uncle had taken relative to the care of Charlie. The fact that he set up a trust for him had really affected my dad emotionally. "What a wonderful, noble thing to do." With a sincere effort to hold back tears, he simply said "Ray, during prayers tonight, you need to thank our maker for your uncle; but above all, thank him for allowing us the privilege of being raised by a man with values and a huge heart. Your uncle has always displayed compassion for others. He doesn't view helping people as a burden. To uncle, it's a blessing and a privilege. He's not perfect by any means, but his heart is in the right place."

So, I simply asked my dad, "Is it possible his life was meant to be so complicated?"

Dad replied, "Possibly, but that's another question I am too exhausted to answer tonight, but I will certainly give it some thought and we'll discuss it later."

Friday morning was cold, with heavy snow falling. Two or three inches accumulation was already on the ground. Uncle's wish was being granted. The entire week was uncommonly calm and void of any conflict or unrealistic expectations. The following morning it was clear my father had changed the station on the radio. We were listening to big band music by Glenn Miller. Mom danced around the kitchen, indicating she was in a better mood. Even my sister seemed more alert and docile.

The atmosphere was relaxing and with everyone's mood elevated and calmer, Dad actually appeared enthusiastic about the snow, saying, "Finally it's decided to be winter."

Mom quickly responded, "Well it comes regardless of your preference." I heard uncle stomping the snow off his packs before entering the kitchen. He looked bright-eyed, bushy-tailed and ready to face the day with enthusiasm and optimism. Sitting down at the table, he asked for coffee while pulling on Cindy's braids. She never objected to uncle tugging on her braids because she thrived on his attention. He was warming up the Nash, saying he wanted give us a ride to school. He also offered to pick up our friends along the way. Where in the hell that came from no one dared to ask. Simply put, his disposition radiated a renewed zest for life. How that transition happened so quickly was certainly confusing to Mom and especially Dad. They both welcomed his optimism, which seemed to further elevate everyone's disposition and mood. With Mom providing some last-minute instructions, Sis, uncle and I walked toward his Nash. I looked back just in time to see Mom snapping a photo of us walking hand-in-hand with our loving, well-groomed uncle.

When we arrived at school with a carload of warm and happy students, I was most surprised because uncle parked and then got out with us. He started walking along with Sis toward the entrance. I wondered what was going on with my uncle but didn't have the courage to ask. He opened the door, letting everyone inside, and then he followed. He walked carefree toward the principal's office. He removed his cap when

Miss Stone walked into the hall. I must say Miss Stone appeared more attractive this morning with her hair piled neatly on top of her head. I noticed she even wore high heels instead of her usual flats or loafers. She completely ignored me walking toward uncle, saying, "Good morning, Lee. There's a great movie playing at the Shines Theatre that starts at seven o'clock tonight."

He replied, "Great. We'll have dinner at the Silver Grill about five o'clock."

She replied, "Fine. I'll see you then." She turned and walked back into her office as uncle watched her walk away. I stood there totally mesmerized until uncle winked, put on his cap and left school.

Walking toward class, I recalled uncle saying, "Maybe you can teach an old dog new tricks," and smiled as I walked toward the cloak room.

With the school day over, it was still snowing with no indication of letting up. Walking home with my friends, we decided to take the sidewalk because Joey had timed the shortcut which turned out to be five minutes longer! Joey always felt the shortcut was longer. Leave it to him to take the time to prove he was right.

Upon my return home, I noticed the Nash was gone, along with Dad's Chevy. When I walked inside, my mom welcomed me enthusiastically. She handed me my hunting clothes, saying, "Ray, your dad and uncle need your help down the Dusty Trail."

I asked, "Why?"

She simply replied, "Your father has a buck down and they're dragging it out. He wants you to head down as soon as possible." I rushed with excitement and I ran as fast as I could toward the orchard. The snow was easing up, making it feel warmer, but it was probably adrenalin, plus sprinting with excitement. Reaching the two vehicles, I saw Dad dragging a huge rack buck slowly through the snow.

He stopped to rest and that's when he saw me running in his direction. My uncle was so elated with Dad's success he proudly said, "Ray, this is your dad's first real trophy buck, thanks to you." Dad was ecstatic and grinned from ear-to-ear with a huge sense of accomplishment. Counting the points, this buck was a legal eleven-point with massive front and hindquarters. Hearing another vehicle, all three of us looked in that direction. Two of Dad's brothers walked toward us, hollering in excitement for my father. My mom must have also called them for help. Admiring the trophy and discussing his possible weight, they grabbed the deer, dragging it toward one of my uncle's trucks. With the buck loaded, uncle looked at his watch, saying, "You guys hang him, because I'm expected somewhere in a half hour."

While getting into his Nash, Dad and his brothers said in unison, "What in the hell is going on with him? It's so unusual for him to leave with a huge rack like this being taken by a family member."

I recall thinking to myself, "It's really true about a pretty woman and venison, in that order." With photos taken and some beer shared in the shed, my uncles left for supper while Dad and I discussed his afternoon hunt. My sister had joined us, sitting on Dad's lap, and she asked if that buck was the Grey Ghost.

Dad laughed and said, "No, Cindy, that's not the Ghost." We walked back home admiring Dad's first trophy rack.

That evening after supper several uncles and friends showed up to celebrate Dad's success. My father and his brothers weighed the deer and it dressed out at two hundred and fifteen pounds. After sitting around the kitchen table with Dad's brothers, they talked about how they were all surprised at uncle's mysterious disappearance. Shortly after that discussion, we heard more traffic on the porch and uncle walked inside escorting my principal. Honestly, you could have heard a pin drop until my sister said, "Wow, this is really neat." Mom immediately became the gracious hostess, smiling as she introduced Miss Stone to the others.

With everyone excusing themselves as they left the house, I overheard Uncle Don say, "That old uncle of ours must be in the rut." Every one of my uncles laughed hysterically as they left for home. Uncle and Miss Stone admired Dad's deer and said their goodbyes as they left for the movies.

Later that evening before going to bed, I overheard mom say to Dad, "You know those two are a perfect fit."

Dad said, "Ethel, you're absolutely right again. Miss Stone is very nice and gracious." He also added, "She's really classy." There was little fanfare that evening going to bed except when Dad mentioned the plans for the morning were for us to leave around eight o'clock a.m. I drifted off to sleep quickly with feelings of relaxation and anticipation.

Saturday morning at seven o'clock, I was looking out the window admiring Dad's buck, but I was also checking to see if uncle was having his morning coffee with breakfast. The light was on in the kitchen indicating he was up and moving around the house. The chimney was smoking, since some wood had obviously been placed in uncle's stove. I walked downstairs and was greeted by Mom, who appeared well rested and wearing a heavy new pink bathrobe. Cindy was sitting at the table with her blanket wrapped around her shoulders. My dad cooked the eggs and I could see the bacon was already finished, as it was sitting on the stove on low. Dad was concentrating on scrambling the eggs while Mom sat enjoying her coffee. Thinking back on mornings like that always stir strong emotional memories that will never be captured again. With breakfast over, uncle walked inside, dressed in his hunting attire. He had an expression on his face that indicated enthusiasm and a need to get started without any interruption or for that matter, confusion.

He appeared to be all business, which Dad picked up on, saying, "We're about ready." Getting into the Nash, we were given instructions by uncle regarding how we were to approach the wagons and how Dad should walk and approach his small tree stand at the end of the swamp. My uncle said the wind would be pretty still, along with partly cloudy skies. There was a possibility of snow. The temperature was forecast for a high of thirty-six degrees. My father said, "The conditions are perfect. Let's hope the Ghost is taking the route you expect."

Uncle nodded and replied, "We'll know in a few hours." With evidence of several hunters parked along the roads, it appeared every serious deer hunter was taking advantage of the fresh snow and mild weather. Pulling into Clayton's drive, Dad got out and opened the gate. Uncle drove ahead while scanning the meadows and cornfields. With Dad back in the Nash, my uncle checked his watch, saying, "It's nine o'clock, so we're right on schedule. Let's hope the Ghost is preparing for his last Saturday brunch!" Driving slowly he pulled over, turned off the car and explained we would walk from there. I was transfixed by uncle's intensity, along with Dad's concentration. This was really serious business; not just another deer hunt. I could see that my uncle and Dad had something to prove. They took their guns out of the cases, loaded them and made certain the safeties were on. Then they put their guns under their arms with barrels down and we started walking slowly toward the swamp. Uncle seemed nervous, which surprised me. He said, "Don't walk too fast or you'll sweat, giving off odor, plus you'll get chilled very quickly." This entire process was intriguing. With the ongoing intensity I felt slightly out of place. Dad kept watching the meadows just in case the Ghost might appear out of nowhere. Uncle said ,"Whatever you do, don't shoot anything other than the Ghost. We already have venison, so let's concentrate only on the Grey bastard for a few days. With only a quarter mile or so to get to the wagons, uncle told Dad to approach his stand from further down than normal, so my father left us to swing to his right and approach his stand slowly, giving uncle and me time to work our way to the wagons. Uncle walked slowly and intently looking around as he checked the wind direction. He whispered, "The wind is very still. I hope the clouds roll through. We could really use some sunshine. That will drive the other hunters out of the woods."

I was trying to comprehend his thinking, but the concept confused me even more. I wondered how often this old uncle had approached other hunts in a similar manner. His knowledge and experience were obviously based on doing, not talking. It was acutely evident this rustic outdoorsman had walked the walk without the talk. Uncle was on a mission and my father had also signed on for a significant role. Working our way to our wagon, uncle pointed to two fresh doe tracks. He lowered his head and whispered in my ear, "Those does were here around an hour ago." How he knew that was beyond me. Getting to the wagons, he put his rifle on the floor of the wagon after unloading it. Uncle lifted himself up and after gaining his balance, put out his hand and helped me up onto the wagon. His intensity was so pervasive it was a bit unnerving. Brushing the snow off the hay bale seats, he told me to sit on the left kitty corner so I could watch some of the hedgerow along with the corner of the cornfield. He whispered, "If you see or hear anything, just move your right hand sideways so I can see it. If you smell a buck, turn your thumb up until I see your indicator."

I whispered, "Okay," so he sat down behind the bales with just our eyes and foreheads showing above the highest bales. He had arranged some spaces between the bales for shooting, especially the one he expected to use in the shooting lane cut five days earlier. Maybe it was six days. Somehow I lost track. Settling down, it was evident we were positioned correctly as far as uncle was concerned.

CHAPTER 30

The Complicated Hunt

The swamp birch, cedar and tag alders were laden with snow, causing poor visibility into the swamp. Uncle sat motionless as he intently scanned the entire area. A light breeze was blowing out of the swamp and a couple of chickadees flew onto the bales to feed. One brave bird landed on uncle's cap and he never even flinched. I was captivated by that moment, thinking about the unbelievable degree of concentration my uncle possessed. I took note of the extreme attention paid to every single detail by my uncle. He obviously knew those extremes would help increase our odds. Heavy dark clouds were looming above, indicating possible snow showers. It wasn't very cold, so sitting completely still didn't create a problem. Watching my area intensely, I realized if I screwed up it might be a disaster. The pressure was on! Uncle had usually been very patient with me, but today I felt insecure, realizing the fierce significance of this hunt. I was putting a great deal of pressure on myself. I started wondering about my father thinking about his trophy buck hanging back at uncle's home. I heard some geese flying over the farm as they made their yearly flight south and somehow I felt comforted. I remembered learning in school why they flew in a "V" formation.

We sat there for an hour, which felt more like days without any activity other than the pesky birds feeding on the hay bails. Uncle twisted his wrist to check his watch, and it was ten-thirty. Slowly leaning his head in my direction, he said in a whisper, "It's time to get serious." I vividly remember thinking how in the hell was I expected to get any more serious than I already was? I was jolted back to reality smelling deer; however, the smell indicated does. Moving my right hand from side-to-side, uncle simply nodded. The smell provided some anticipation, along with badly needed motivation. Uncle again nodded slowly, but kept scanning the swamp intently. Within three or four minutes, two does appeared, feeding just inside the hedgerow near the edge of the swamp. Those deer seemed very relaxed as they kept their heads down feeding. Both does were of decent size. Their reddish-brown color painted a gorgeous winter scene against the white snow. My God, they were a sight to behold, with one feeding head down as the other one raised her head with ears standing straight up checking her surroundings. After looking around, she lowered her head more slowly and started to feed again. While we were watching the does, the wind shifted and began blowing briskly in the opposite direction, which affected my nose ability. It was almost impossible to detect any deer smell coming out of the swamp. It seemed to be of little concern to uncle because he was still closely scanning the swamp with his dark brown eyes. His objective remained fixed on our primary purpose. He had forgotten about the does because they certainly weren't his target.

The wind suddenly came up, blowing the heavy snow off the branches. That helped startle the does and they bounced down toward Dad's tree stand out of my sight. Uncle took that opportunity to check his watch and it was eleven-thirty. I was getting cold and becoming restless and somewhat impatient. Hearing a shot off in the distance with the wind blowing into our backs, I also heard the traffic on the highway. I felt uncle was probably disappointed with the change in wind direction, because it was going to make his well-thought-out theory much less effective. I could hear Clayton's tractor start up as more flocks of geese flew overhead. I wondered if Dad had seen the does. Without warning, a very strong pungent odor filled my nostrils. It was strong and obviously the smell of a buck, but it seemed to be coming from a different direction than I expected. The deer was behind us. I figured the smell was probably coming from the cornfield I was watching, but I couldn't see anything that resembled a deer. Excitingly, I put up my thumb which uncle fortunately noticed. He was instantly on alert, becoming rigid and tense. I didn't dare move, even to blink an eye. It had to be the Ghost because it smelled so strong. The Ghost smelled much stronger today than I remembered. My heart was pounding and racing out of control, while uncle sat motionless and perfectly still. I noticed beads of sweat forming on his forehead and upper lip. That vision has haunted me every time I see a buck or think back about that day.

Snow continued falling off the trees, making me extremely jumpy and nervous, but my uncle seemed calm, yet intense at the same time. Uncle never tried to make any attempt to turn around. He was being careful not to spook the Ghost. He knew I was also aware that any movement or noise was out of the question. Thankfully, uncle realized I was capable of being involved in this most serious objective. My natural instinct was to turn slightly, but that was out of the question. Sitting completely motionless, my insides were shaking and my right hand trembled uncontrollably. With my eyes fixed on the edge of the cornfield, I suddenly saw a huge rack come into view, moving slowly. I could not make out a body. I blinked to adjust my vision but still couldn't see his body. The Ghost was walking in a small ditch. His rack was mammoth as he deliberately moved. Then his head and front shoulders suddenly appeared as he walked out of the ditch. It was certainly the magnificent Grey Ghost. There was, however, a serious problem. My uncle had his back to him but he was acutely aware and knew enough not to make any attempt to turn around. This situation certainly wasn't expected, but it was what it was. Uncle was conscious of the wind direction, so he understood his predicament. I didn't dare take my eyes off this huge deer. The Ghost raised his huge rack, looking around, seeming comfortable and confident. He continued walking slowly toward the hedgerow and then stopped, appearing utterly on alert, which made me very nervous.

I heard Clayton's tractor moving slowly in our direction and I thought perhaps the sound would drive the Ghost down into the hedgerow in our direction toward the swamp. That buck was so huge he appeared to be unnatural. Even after seeing Dad's trophy buck yesterday, this buck was much larger in every single detail. The Ghost was getting close enough for me to see muscles protruding from his front legs and his hindquarters. Muscles rippled on this buck just like they do on a beefy, well-built weightlifter. The Grey Ghost was only eighty yards from the wagon. So close, yet so far away. That buck stood straight and tall, with his rack accentuating his dominance. With his rack waving into the air, he seemed to scan the area looking around. As he stomped his right leg, I felt he was showing that he was in control.

Then, without any warning, he jumped aggressively into the start of the hedgerow. He stopped again, raising his head to look around. The Ghost knew something was amiss, but regardless, he made the mistake of slowly calming down. At that point, uncle had taken a serious chance and rotated slightly, realizing what was transpiring before my eyes. I knew by moving, uncle now had a view of the Ghost. I was still in the way for him to get a good shot. I know I could have shot him myself without any trouble during the last ten minutes. This situation was so intense my bladder needed draining and I fought to ignore the urge. There was no doubt in my mind the Ghost sensed something was different, yet one step at a time, he walked down the hedgerow exuding confidence. The massive white tail was only fifty yards away and that placed him directly in front of me. I could see steam coming out of his nostrils and his smell was so intense it was obnoxious. Uncle slowly positioned himself, moving ever-so-slightly to his left. Realizing he was forced to wait, he lifted his rifle slowly, resting it on the bale. He sat waiting for his opportunity. One step at a time, this huge deer moved closer toward his potential demise. Uncle was breathing very heavily with excitement. Suddenly, the Ghost was within just fifteen yards of the shooting lane uncle had cut. With one bounce he was within five yards. My uncle was prepared for anything as he looked through his open sights waiting for the precise moment. He was shaking from the tension. Uncle was also breathing quickly in an effort to stay calm. The Ghost took two more steps then stopped and looked around again, lifting his rack into the air.

Feeling secure, his right shoulder stepped into the shooting lane. I watched uncle take a long deep breath before moving the rifle slightly to his right. Uncle pulled the trigger and the shot rang out. The entire area went completely still, which felt a bit mystical. The Ghost flinched slightly, acting surprised, while uncle racked another shell into the thirty-thirty. Before my uncle could get off another shot, the ghost simply looked toward the wagon and in one huge bounce disappeared into the swamp. Shaking with intense excitement, uncle lowered his rifle, setting it down roughly on the bales with disgust. With disappointment quickly surfacing on his face, he muttered almost to himself, "How in the hell could

I have missed that old bastard? He certainly didn't act hit."
In disbelief, my uncle sat down, appearing weakened by the
reality that perhaps his chance had eluded him. I was rendered
speechless, along with recalling the entire event over again
as I tried to digest the distinct possibility that our one chance
resulted in failure.

Dad was running quickly toward the wagon yelling, "Is
he down?"

Uncle just sat there on the bale until he replied, "I think I
missed. He made it back into the swamp."

Dad appeared more optimistic as he said, "I saw the
whole thing. You couldn't have missed." Dad walked toward
the shooting lane to check for blood and hair. Uncle just sat
there paralyzed from shock and obvious disappointment. My
dad yelled excitingly, "He's hit! There's blood and hair everywhere." As Dad started toward the swamp, my uncle still
seemed to be dazed by feelings of failure. With the blood and
hair sighting indicating the possibility of success he showed
some relief. With Dad's complete optimism, uncle appeared
to have a renewed interest in the reality that the Ghost was
hit.

After yelling to Dad instructing him not to go into the
swamp, uncle said, "That wounded bastard is tough." He also
indicated that he would be right down. I was completely ignored due to all of the emotion and adrenalin flowing from
all three of us. Uncle tried very hard to regain his strength
as he accepted the reality that he would require a clear head
to focus completely on his objective. This entire sequence of
events had been completely unexpected. These circumstances
made me more focused on the potential problems we were
facing. I was speechless and I felt completely helpless. My
father reluctantly returned to the wagon. He was aware of the
need to understand my uncle's position and his reaction to

what had occurred. Wounding this trophy buck was creating some strong, yet negative reactions from Uncle Lee. Regaining proper perspective was absolutely essential. After a few seconds my uncle showed a sense of renewed energy. I believe the reality of the problem was slowly seeping into my uncle's brain. Finally, he wisely said, "Let's give the Ghost thirty minutes to lay down and bleed out. He needs to lose some of his will and his massive strength."

My father appeared intensely deep in thought. He became proactive and decided to speak up and take over. He never hesitated for one second as he said, "Uncle, we need to get more help. Any way you look at this situation, we're in serious trouble. One way or another this is going to require experienced hunters. I'm going to call my brothers for help."

Uncle agreed and responded, "You're right. Even if he's down, we're still going to require strong bodies to drag him out of the damn swamp. Tell your brothers to wear waders, bring flashlights and lots of energy."

We were grateful as we suddenly heard Clayton yelling from the cornfield, asking if we needed help. My father met him halfway up the slight grade explaining what the situation was. Clayton offered to take care of calling the men to get the word out. He indicated that he also felt it would be almost impossible to locate the Ghost without a serious search party using at least six experienced hunters. Uncle never offered a rebuttal or even shared an opinion. He knew and agreed with his friend because he realized the complications relative to tracking and finding this record-breaking trophy white tail. Uncle looked at his watch appearing very concerned. It was now close to one o'clock. He shook his head, saying, "Let's hurry! By the time this plan gets implemented, daylight will be a serious issue." While Clayton left to make the necessary calls, the three of us sat there obviously pensive and very anxious. Thinking out loud for some unexplained reason, I verbalized an idea which created some controversy.

Neither uncle nor Dad were paying much attention to what I had to say until they heard, "Bring the redbone. That hound loves tracking deer."

Dad said, "Ray, that's a great idea, if we can't find the Ghost, we'll use the hound as a last resort. What in the hell do we care if it's legal or not, that buck needs to be found; he's not just some typical wounded deer."

After hearing Dad's opinion, uncle laughed, saying, "You're right. Drive home and get the redbone." With that idea considered, my uncle knew we had a serious chance of finding the Ghost. Uncle grabbed my hand, saying, "Ray, your nose ability, staying calm and thinking concisely has been a real asset. Your suggestion will probably work, but let's agree to keep the redbone idea to ourselves." Uncle explained, "I don't think this is legal, but understand this buck shouldn't die in vain and just rot in the swamp. This hunt is no longer about us; it's simply a fact that the old bastard should be recognized for his will to live, along with his unique size. The Grey Ghost deserves to be admired and recognized along with a record of his actual existence. He deserves to go down in the archives of local history. The buck is a legend in this area, though some people doubt his existence. He deserves a place in the record books."

With Dad heading to get the hound, along with more family help on the way, my uncle seemed much more coherent and relaxed. Ironically, at the same time he also appeared very impatient. He started pacing in an attempt to work off his anxiety. I knew he was thinking within the realm of possibilities that this attempt could still fail. Even though it had been concluded by the adults that this buck would be found, there were no guarantees.

Clayton returned driving his truck through the cornfields and rejoined us at the wagon. He called two of uncle's nephews and they were excited and happy to help. He also mentioned that they were arranging a search party. Clayton appeared fixated on the attempt to find the buck, offering, "Lee, whatever it takes to get it done."

Uncle thanked his friend, stating, "I know you're aware of the significance of this trophy and you understand this is no longer about the hunt. It's our responsibility to give this buck the respect he deserves."

Clayton said, "This buck will stand this entire hunting community on it's ear. Isn't it most fitting that the Grey Ghost remains a challenge even in his death?"

A few minutes later, six of my uncles plus dad and the redbone were preparing for the assault into the swamp. They were all enthusiastic and confident, telling my grateful uncle to have patience and stay calm. Uncle stopped their first attempt, yelling, "Take the hound, because daylight is diminishing rapidly."

One of my uncles asked, "Are you sure about that? That old hound isn't in the best of shape."

Uncle Lee stood his ground as he said, "Who the heck is?" With the hound leashed, they lined up twenty feet apart as they started into the swamp talking to each other and trying to remain composed with a sense of purpose. Every one of those men were young, experienced and most of all willing to do what it would take to return with the Grey Ghost.

I heard Dad yell, "The hound's got his track," which improved uncle's confidence. It also indicated that the search party's first objective was met. That was the last thing we heard for over an hour.

Sitting with Clayton and uncle on the wagon, the conversation went from feelings of anxiety to the frustrations of helplessness. Neither of those old friends were used to the fact they had been forced to the sidelines. Both men knew why, but they were having problems accepting their limited roles and they were not very comfortable with that revelation. While daylight was still available, my father walked out of the swamp carrying the redbone in his arms saying, "We found him two miles inside. It's going to take an act of God to drag that buck out in less than four hours."

Dad said, "It's terrible in there. In fact, worse than we thought. It's so thick in there that it's beyond all of us how he survived. This poor dog is sick from exhaustion and needs to get to a Vet right away.

Clayton said, "Put him in the truck. My Vet is just down the road." My uncle was worried and seemed more concerned with the condition of the redbone than he was with the realization that they had actually found the Grey Ghost. Dad was soaked wet from head to toe, along with being plastered with mud. He appeared exhausted, yet at the same time he was also ecstatic.

Putting the hound carefully into the truck, Dad said "This buck weighs well over three hundred pounds. It's hard to grasp, but his rack is fourteen perfect points with moss still growing around the base. Wait until you see this buck up close. It gives me the willies just thinking about how majestic the Ghost really is." My dad turned back toward the swamp with his flashlight, saying, "Ray, if you're cold, go to Clayton's."

While Clayton drove the redbone to the Vet, he also offered to call Mom. My uncle and I were both tired and cold, as well as emotionally drained. Sitting anxiously together on the bales, we heard vehicles and saw several sets of headlights heading down the tote roads. These vehicles were heading toward the swamp. Evidently, the word was out. People arrived one after another, working their way toward my reluctant uncle. He certainly didn't want or need curiosity seekers interfering and speculating about this complicated, yet successful hunt.

CHAPTER 31

Accept Life on Life's Terms

The last thing we needed or expected at that time was a crowd speculating about the buck. They didn't need to share their ignorant opinions, which they certainly wouldn't know enough to keep to themselves. My uncle never understood Monday morning quarterbacks. He just sat down and appeared to be extremely disgusted with the boldness and intrusiveness of others. Clayton's farm was posted legally, however, that obviously didn't stop unwelcome intruders. He was noticeably aggravated as he walked toward uncle saying, "Lee, this is about you and your family. I'm going to put a stop to this circus before it goes any further."

Uncle looked at his friend, saying, "Just let my family members come down to observe, some of the wives may show up. I'm not at all in the mood to deal with any crap right now, since it's been such a roller coaster ride. I need time to digest, think and make plans to deal with the intense interest this buck is going to create."

Clayton assertively started toward the uninvited spectators, saying, "Please leave my property. Don't force me to call the authorities." Reluctantly, as they complained, the vehicles started leaving the cornfield. Uncle continued to sit there, tired, cold and hungry. The adrenalin rush had zapped all of his energy. He appeared slightly disengaged from his victory and I think he seemed disappointed for some unexplained reason. I, on the other hand, sincerely hoped he would comprehend his accomplishment and start relishing in the glory. After all, he finally bagged a record-breaking trophy buck. I am sure he knew his reaction was unexpected, so he finally reached over and patted my knee for reassurance as he affectionately said, "I've got some mixed emotions about ending the Ghost's life." I observed uncle's reservations first-hand, and from that perspective, he appeared to be feeling some remorse after harvesting the buck. After all, uncle had religiously stalked this elusive buck for several years. In some respect, they had established a strange, yet special relationship. With some reluctance, uncle sat there silently waiting to witness his trophy being dragged out of the swamp by his nephews. My own personal reaction towards my uncle's letdown started creeping into my feelings of accomplishment.

Clayton returned after closing the gate and walked up to the wagon, saying, "Lee, I just heard from my wife. There will be a game warden and newspaper reporter here shortly. Jim called to say he's on his way to document and get all the details of your success."

Uncle laughed with that news, replying, "That figures! Instead of trying to catch jackers, he wants the publicity of getting recognized for actually being on the job." Uncle went on, "Some thing's just never change. Jim's a nice man; however, he's always looking for publicity. I've got my tag and the dog is at the Vet, so we're legal and that's all that matters right now."

Clayton replied, "Are you prepared for all the publicity this buck is going to generate? I hope you're aware that news travels fast these days."

Uncle thought about that for several minutes, then responded saying, "It's kind of late to worry about any inconvenience to me. This is your land and you're right in the middle of this fiasco. Is that alright with you?"

Clayton just said, "Lee we've been friends since childhood. This certainly isn't a problem. I'm just happy you're the one that finally bagged this trophy. You of all people know the actual existence of this deer has been debated for quite some time."

Uncle Lee responded, "I know, and here we are standing around trying to regain interest in the purpose. I find myself thinking about how neither one of us is very good at just waiting. It's certainly not easy admitting we're getting old. How long have the boys been in that swamp anyway?"

Clayton replied, "Too long, just over three hours."

Within just a few minutes after that conversation, we heard voices in the swamp and suddenly Dad appeared with his flashlight raised in victory, saying, "Come on down. We've got him within twenty-five yards." The two old friends slid off the wagon making their way toward Dad and his brothers. Uncle's nephews appeared, dragging and trying to carry the ghost. The vision of their effort merits description. Four were dragging while two others cleared brush and obstacles. They worked diligently as a team. Every one of those men were mud from head-to-toe. They appeared completely exhausted but remained determined. Finally, the boys dropped the Ghost, laying him at the feet of my uncle and his friend Clayton. My father walked toward me, taking my hand while his exhausted brothers lay on the snow-covered ground catching their breath. One uncle asked for a cold beer, which Clayton had anticipated. He rushed over to get a case of Black Label from his truck. That gesture of respect was greeted with cheers from my ecstatic uncles.

Uncle Lee walked around his trophy, admiring every detail before saying, "Isn't this buck a majestic specimen?

He's absolutely unbelievable." My uncle appeared to be satisfied as he hugged each of the men he had nurtured and raised as sons. It had been a long time since all seven had been together in such an effort. Out of respect and loyalty, they lifted uncle carefully in their arms and held him up as a symbol of their love and victory. My Uncle Merlin, who was very sentimental, started singing "Old Danny Boy," which was the family's traditional song used for displaying brotherhood. It was very emotional and quite the sight to behold.

One of my younger uncles grabbed me and put me on his shoulders, saying, "Ray, from what I heard your nose is the key to this jubilant moment. You should be on cloud nine taking credit with Uncle Lee."

That celebration lasted until the game warden and newspaper reporter arrived to put a damper on our activity. The party was over when my uncle tagged his trophy legally, asking for a volunteer to gut the huge buck. It was pitch black, but with flashlights, the chore was accomplished. With the deer dressed, the reporter started firing questions. That was short-lived when uncle interrupted, saying, "These boys need dry clothes and rest. You're welcome to stop over in the morning." Uncle was trying to be gracious, but the young reporter was persistent. The reporter's lack of understanding caused uncle to lose it and become angry. Firmly putting his fist under the reporter's nose, he assertively ranted, "You're totally unaware of what's going on here. You live in an ivory tower which leads you to be oblivious of the needs of others. Get the hell out of my way before I personally drag your white shirt and suit through the mud, which will give me great pleasure." The conversation stopped when it became clear uncle was serious. All of my uncles just smiled with their memories of seeing uncle upset before.

The game warden was more perceptive as he said, "Calm down, Lee, I do need some information. Looking at these boys, there's no reason it can't wait until morning." The game warden followed that by respectfully putting out his hand and uncle shook it as a courtesy.

Then my uncle said, "Let's get out of here and weigh this buck. Would you like to witness the weigh-in?"

Jim offered, "I have official scales. Let's weigh him in Clayton's barn."

The game warden said, "Lee, I'm predicting that this buck will break several records. If you're serious about allowing me to be sanctioned, then fill out the proper paperwork. It's not for me. It's out of respect for this buck's actual existence. Do your job and we'll talk in the morning about the details. Right now the boys need heat, food and rest. Do you understand?"

Jim respectfully said, "Yes. Let me offer my congratulations. You and this deer will become legends and each deserve a place in the record books."

With that comment, I believe a tear formed in uncle's eye while he simply replied, "Thank you very much."

With the deer weighing in at two hundred and seventy-two pounds, everyone started for uncle's place to hang the trophy alongside Dad's buck. With that accomplished, I said good night to my family and walked next door. I wanted to get home, prepare for bed and fall asleep, which surprised both of my parents. Honestly, the intensity of the entire day had literally exhausted me to a point that I had lost the desire to participate any further. It spite of being tired, I still had difficulty falling asleep. It was virtually impossible to avoid all the activity taking place next door! With a sense of satisfaction the vision of that majestic buck finally helped me drift off to sleep.

Waking at around seven o'clock a.m., it was apparent this morning would be filled with confusion created by the massive buck. Slipping on my robe, I looked out the window and counted at least fifty adults admiring and discussing the trophy. There was no sign of my uncle. Dad stood with Leo, Weasel and Simon. It appeared my father was quite engaged as he explained every single detail to the old codgers.

For some unexplained reason I felt a bit reluctant to face the morning, as I wondered if uncle was experiencing the same feelings as me. As I walked into the kitchen Mom greeted me, saying, "Well Ray, you, your uncle and your father are celebrities this morning." With her delivery, it was apparent something wasn't right.

I asked, "Where's uncle and what's the problem?"

Mom said, "Your Uncle Lee went to pick up the hound at the Vet. He doesn't respond well to mass confusion, so this may be a difficult day for him. Get dressed and eat breakfast, because I think he's going to need your support and understanding." Mom also said, "Ray, I'm concerned that this situation is going to create an emotional letdown for your uncle." From Mom's observation it became obvious that no one realized that his success could ultimately end his desire to pursue whitetails ever again. I mean, how could anyone possibly ever top this experience? While eating breakfast, I sat there contemplating how this day might evolve as I tried to comprehend and anticipate uncle's unexpected reaction. Suddenly, it dawned on me what was transpiring. Mom was having coffee sitting alongside Sis and I, so I shared my thoughts on the situation.

I explained by saying, "Mom, it's like Christmas Day. After all the preparation and anticipation that goes into making it a great celebration, the big day arrives. Then, all the gifts are opened and in a flash, it's over. That always makes me sad, but getting ready for church always renews my feelings as I think about the true meaning of the day."

Mom smiled, saying, "Ray, you're too smart for your own good. That's exactly what uncle's experiencing."

Dad walked inside asking for a cup of coffee and muttering to himself, "There are cars lined up and down both sides of the street. It's hard to believe how much interest the Grey Ghost has generated. With some concern showing on Dad's face, he said, "I certainly hope the redbone is all right. Where's uncle?"

I said, "From the looks of things, he probably can't get into his own drive," which made my father laugh.

Dressed in warm clothes, Dad and I walked onto the porch to contemplate our next move. Simply put, there were so many spectators Dad said, "This really puts the icing on the cake. When your uncle sees this mess it's going to set him off. Ray, we both know how uncle is regarding his own personal privacy. Why don't we clear out his yard and close the driveway. This will help eliminate some disorder." Dad yelled above the beehive of activity, "All right everybody, the party's over. Clear out before I'm forced to call the police. Please leave the property and give our family the privacy we need and deserve."

One belligerent male asked, "What's it to you? This isn't your property!"

So Dad simply walked off the porch saying, "Well if you're not going to respect my request, you leave me just two choices: which one would you like?"

The man's wife said, "It's time to leave. That nephew of Lee's means business."

Fortunately for that man, four game wardens walking up the street had overheard the conversation, saying, "All right everyone, this is official state business. Leave the area at once."

That display cleared out the area quickly after the traffic jam was resolved. The game wardens walked around the buck measuring every detail, along with recording their information on a yellow legal pad. They were pleasant along with being captivated by the Grey Ghost's size and weight. His rack was also of special interest, being measured in every detail. One of the wardens walked in my direction, asking where Uncle Lee was. Before I could respond, the Nash pulled into the drive.

Getting out, my uncle acknowledged the men, saying, "Let me take care of this hound before we start discussing the deer."

Jim walked toward uncle, asking what the hound's name was. Uncle smiled, offering, "Red Bone."

Then Jim replied, "I know his breed, but what's his name?"

Uncle smiled again, offering, "Jim, we call him Red Bone."

All the game wardens laughed until Jim replied, "How could I be so stupid! That makes perfect sense."

Uncle walked toward me and handed me the leash saying, "Take him inside and feed him and make sure he has water before he falls asleep." It never occurred to anyone why the hound was exhausted, thank the lord.

Uncle invited the men into the shed, asking, "What's on your agenda in respect to this deer's place in the record books?"

"Well, we have two options. Let's go inside and we'll explain your options in detail," said the warden.

Uncle yelled, "Hurry Ray! I want your opinion and your father's, as well." After getting the redbone situated, I walked into the trapper's shed noticing how the men were admiring the fur along with the two trophy bucks hanging outside. Even with all of their experience on the job, it was very apparent to these game wardens they were in the presence of a legend in his own time.

Making out the paperwork, one of the wardens said, "Lee, I took the liberty to call Albany last night and the head of the Department of Wildlife wants me to offer you a proposal. Would you be interested in donating this deer to be mounted full body and displayed in the headquarters of the state capital? There is considerable interest in preserving such a unique specimen. Would you consider that option or are you planning on mounting and keeping this trophy in the family, which I would completely understand?"

Uncle sat back looked at me and said, "Ray, do you comprehend their offer?"

I replied, "Yes. Donate the deer because it seems to be the right thing to do out of respect for the Ghost and your relationship with him."

Uncle sat up, looking at Dad, saying, "Well then, donate it is! That's really the right thing to do and it's a very noble ending for this majestic buck." With uncle and Dad signing the pile of paperwork, I slowly walked outside deciding to take one last walk around the Ghost before the game wardens took him to his destination in preparation for his place in history. I was filled with gratitude, along with trying to grasp the significance of our decision.

Looking at the deer from head to foot, I excitedly ran back into the shed yelling, "Uncle, come here, we need to talk!"

He asked, "Ray, what's the problem?" as I grabbed his hand trying to drag him out of the shed. He excused himself, looking very confused by my assertiveness. Walking outside, I pulled uncle toward the buck, and that's when it suddenly dawned on uncle why I was so ecstatic and energized. That buck had a right dewclaw. This buck wasn't the Ghost after all. My uncle started to laugh hysterically, yelling to everyone, "Come on out. This is going to create a renewed interest in this buck."

Dad started laughing while the game wardens looked completely baffled, probably thinking we were a bit crazy until uncle said, "You guys won't understand because this is an inside family joke."

After the game wardens left that day, my uncle allowed anyone who was interested to photograph the buck and spend as much time as needed. With a fire burning in the shed, we walked inside to relax. My uncle was calm and seemed at peace within himself, saying, "Sit down, Ray. I need to explain why I selected you to carry on the traditions of this family. Please try to understand this complex obligation and my desire for you to embrace your inherited responsibilities. I've had a story running through my head for years. I had no way to document our family's traditions and love. I sketched trying to capture those moments, and here is the chest filled with my attempt to capture my love of nature, wildlife and our family. These will be put in a vault specially made to preserve art. In my opinion, they're not great, but it's my legacy as I understand it. You're smart and sensitive, along with strong-willed. Simply put, you're a survivor. I've watched you love and nurture our hounds while always appreciating nature, from helping plant the garden to simply looking at a maple leaf in the fall with awe. I could see how you appreciated its color and beauty and I know you realized it's simply a gorgeous thing gifted by our maker. You observe the seasons and relish in the evolution of life Spring brings and the death that Fall offers, never preferring one over the other. You understand the need for both. I've watched you investigate the meaning of life in simple, yet profound ways. You're a young man filled with curiosity and you need to pursue the quest to understand the meaning of life. Ray, you show patience, tolerance and respect naturally. I feel those characteristics will serve you well in the future. I also feel what we have established in this unconditional love you possess for nature and your family and friends will surely enhance your life."

"I also feel you may be destined to fail occasionally. Because you have the capacity to admit failure, you will also recover; stronger, more persistent and you will persevere.

Because of those characteristics, you have given me a renewed purpose in my own life. At my age, it was difficult to stay motivated with an honest sense of purpose to continue forging ahead. I lost my identity a year ago, feeling lost and alone. You may be too young to understand that reality. Over time, this revelation will make perfect sense. I wondered about death and dying, asking when and how. These are normal feelings for people up in age. There are no guarantees in life, as you already know, so prepare for pain in your life, because no one gets out of life unscathed. Always remember that when life gets filled with confusion or sadness, it's time to pull up your britches and regroup. The real meaning of life is so complex that tons of money is spent in the pursuit of happiness. Try to recall what we experienced and what we will continue to experience in the peace and serenity offered within the universal gift of life itself. With our unconditional love for each other, everything is possible, thus giving me the will to live and enjoy your evolution as you grow from year to year.

Someday when you're my age, looking for purpose and reasons to move into each day with optimism, I want you to look back and remember this simple message. If you have a thought or vision that needs expressing, find a way to share your experience, strength and purpose. Above all, stay true to yourself, even in darkness or despair. It's your life while walking down the path least traveled. Always know your namesake and I are always alongside for comfort. It's imperative that you accept life on life's terms, but also realize that a man is remembered by his book."

About the Author

I was born and raised in Massena, New York, which is a small town located along the Saint Lawrence River. I always had a passion for writing from a young age. Nature and wildlife always fascinated me.

I worked for the local paper after college, however, my inability to stay fair and balanced resulted in that career being short-lived. My desire to create was a contradiction to news reporting.

Nature and wildlife photography, coupled with writing, was a passion which brought me several awards. Over the years I published several articles in periodicals related to hunting, fishing, trapping and life in particular. Essays and short stories were published in a variety of publications. I always had a desire to write a novel after retirement, but acute low vision stopped that objective. The Lighthouse of Mana-sota helped bring this dream to life.

My writing style is filled with emotion, coupled with simplicity.